THE LIVES OF WILD BIRDS

BOOKS BY ARETAS A. SAUNDERS

THE LIVES OF WILD BIRDS

A GUIDE TO BIRD SONGS

BIRD SONG

DRAWINGS BY DOMINICK D'OSTILIO

The Lives of Wild Birds

BY ARETAS A. SAUNDERS

DOUBLEDAY & COMPANY, INC.

GARDEN CITY, NEW YORK, 1954

LIBRARY OF CONGRESS CATALOG CARD NUMBER 54–5362

Contents

Contents

Introduction

THE science of ornithology began with the collecting of specimens of birds, and the studies of their dead bodies. This was necessary that we might name accurately, describe, and classify our birds. We who today take pleasure in live birds are indebted to those who did this, for it laid the foundation for our studies of live birds. Biology has been defined as the science of life, or of living things. Ornithology is one branch of that science. That is, the goal of ornithology is to be reached by the study of the living bird, not the dead one. The observer of living birds can be just as much a scientist, or an ornithologist, as the museum man who confines his chief studies to dead birds.

Some of our ornithologists whose main work has been the collection and study of specimens have seemed to look upon the study of live birds with disfavor, at least as to considering it a part of ornithology. Ornithology to them has been the collecting, describing, and measuring of specimens. The study of live birds may be interesting, but why call it ornithology? Ornithology is a branch of science. Science is exact knowledge.

But the study of a live bird that is not in the hand is necessarily inexact.

The answer to this is that while the ideal of science is exact knowledge, the actual practice is inexact. Accuracy is a matter of degree. Even the measurement of a bird skin in a laboratory is only as exact as our eyes and instruments can make it. The study of live birds may be less exact than that of dead ones, but without it ornithology would not be a part of the science of life. The complete characters of any bird are not to be found merely in its dead body. There are also many instincts and habits that are definitely characters of the species to which it belongs. The moment a bird is dead these characters are gone. The geographical range of a species, the migration route it travels, the habitat in which it lives, and the character and location of its nest are all admitted parts of ornithology, and depend on the instincts of the live bird. Our study of dead birds has laid the foundation for that of live ones. The science of ornithology here in America is not nearly complete, but only just begun.

The problem is to know just how much of the observations of bird lovers and field students can be accepted as part of our science. Just when does a field student become an ornithologist? When that field student carefully and conscientiously records what he has observed, as accurately as possible, and contributes his observation in the form of publications available to others, he becomes an ornithologist. Nor is he necessarily an ornithologist of lower grade or lesser degree than one who collects birds and measures bird skins, or studies comparative anatomy. He possesses an equal opportunity to rise to a position of authority in his subject, and authority in some field of bird behavior or ecological relations is fully as scientific as authority in anatomy.

On the other hand I would not admit the field observer who merely sees birds and keeps a list, no matter how accurate his identifications or how large his life list may be. If he has not contributed in some manner to our knowledge of birds, he is still without the wall; a bird lover, or a bird student, perhaps, but not an ornithologist.

Every ornithologist who wishes to have his observations accepted must hold before him the scientific ideal, to seek truth for its own sake, and to serve his chosen science, not that he may gain personal glory, but that the science may progress. With that he should maintain a spirit of full co-operation with others, a willingness to submit data to others working in a particular field, whenever such action will best serve the science, and a readiness to give full credit to others who may have submitted data to him. Such an ideal has not always been held in the past, and a lack of it has, at times, hurt the progress of our science. Co-operation, without personal jealousies, should be kept in mind by all as just as much a part of the scientific ideal as truth and accuracy.

The search for truth requires that the searcher throw aside all thoughts that smack of superstition, and all prejudices or preconceived notions. If his observations lead to some theory, he should search as carefully for facts against it as for those that support it. He should be careful that his statements are not dogmatic. Positive statements are only justified when facts are definitely and finally proved, no matter how strong the feeling that they must be true. When speaking of the behavior of any living creature "always" and "never" are too strong expressions to use. It would be better to say, for example, "I have never known a Robin to nest on the ground" than to say, "Robins never nest on the ground."

Finally the good scientist should know his field, not only from his own observations, but also from what others have observed and put on record. Science is search for knowledge, and ignorance the opposite of knowledge. None of us can know all, but willful ignorance in a chosen field is inexcusable. The literature of ornithology is large and increasing rapidly, but nevertheless those papers whose authors have searched the field carefully to know what others have written are best.

The literature of ornithology is by no means all to be found in popular volumes, easily obtained in any public library. Much of the best is scattered through the back numbers of ornithological journals, and these are not always easily available. Still more may be found in bulletins and other publica-cations of museums or other scientific institutions. Often only a small number of these are printed, and when the supply is exhausted they become hard to get. I have included at the end of this work a bibliography for each chapter. The lists of publications will help the student to learn more about each particular subject. I have not included all articles on each subject that are worthy of study, for to do so would greatly increase the size of this volume. The enthusiastic student will search for and find those publications that pertain to the particular subject in which he is most interested.

At the present time the chief ornithological journals that

have wide circulation in America are the *Auk,* the *Wilson Bulletin,* and the *Condor.* The *Auk* is the organ of the American Ornithologists' Union, an organization to which every serious ornithologist in America should belong. The *Wilson Bulletin,* organ of the Wilson Ornithological Club, originally centered in the Mississippi Valley states, but it has now become practically nationwide, and membership in it is highly recommended. The *Condor,* publication of the Cooper Ornithological Society, centers in California and treats more particularly of Western birds. Many of its articles are of more than local interest, however, and students anywhere will find it of value.

Recently the Wilson Ornithological Club has established a library of ornithological literature, and is rapidly accumulating many books and papers. Club members anywhere may borrow from this library, and it is proving to be a great aid to research in ornithology, and an additional incentive for obtaining membership in this active club.

Several of the bird-banding associations have united in the publication of *Bird Banding.* This magazine is not only of interest to those who do bird banding, but is especially valuable for its reviews of ornithological literature, both American and foreign, more complete than in other publications. The *Audubon Magazine,* formerly *Bird-Lore,* is more popular than scientific, but contains good educational and inspirational articles, and news of the progress of conservation. Its colored covers and photographic illustrations are excellent, and its articles on the season and its breeding and Christmas censuses will interest serious bird students.

For a number of years there existed a summer school of

natural history where the chief object was the study of living organisms in the wild state, out-of-doors. This was the Allegany School of Natural History, located in the Allegany State Park in southwestern New York. During the fourteen summers of this school's existence it was my privilege to teach the courses in ornithology. Today I am interested to note that quite a number of former students at that school are nationally and prominently known for their contributions to ornithology.

At this school, field classes were held once a week, and lasted all day. After a morning of observations we stopped for the noon hour at some shady spot near a spring, and after lunch, and a noonday rest, the spot became an outdoor classroom. There I delivered a series of talks on the various phases of bird life. It is the material of these talks, somewhat embellished and brought up to date, that constitutes the remaining portion of this book.

THE LIVES OF WILD BIRDS

The Identification of Birds in the Field

THE study of birds out of doors must begin with identification. Studies of bird behavior are of little value if the species observed has not been accurately identified. In identifying birds we use not only colors and markings, but also size, shape, habits, habitats, and songs or other sounds produced.

The beginner in bird study, when he has an opportunity to accompany someone who is more experienced in the field, is often discouraged when he notes the ease with which his friend identifies birds. A bird flies by, looking merely black against the sky. Not a trace of color or markings shows. Yet the experienced friend names it instantly as bluebird, starling, flicker, goldfinch, or other. His identification, in the great majority of cases, is right and is not mere snap judgment.

Under such circumstances the experienced observer may not be able to say just why he knows the name of the bird in question, but undoubtedly he is using a combination of factors, such as size, shape, and habit of flight. We often come to know our friends among people so well that we can recognize them at a considerable distance. We can see neither the color of their eyes nor the shape of their features, yet we identify them without question. So it is with the bird. The beginner will have to start with color and markings, and gradually the other factors will take their place. Repeated observations of the same bird will give him a familiarity with it, and after a time he will find that he has acquired that same knowledge that his friend has. Then common birds need no longer be scrutinized closely to be named.

IDENTIFICATION BY COLOR AND MARKINGS

Color and markings are the characters most easily described and the chief ones on which keys in textbooks are based. In determining the colors of a bird, the light conditions and the direction from which the light comes are of the greatest importance. This must be constantly borne in mind by the field student. A bird against the light is likely to look solid black, or if colors seem to show around the edges they are likely to be reflections or iridescent effects, or possibly the effect of a pair of field glasses that are not perfectly achromatic. The light should be at the observer's back, and the bird, if possible, against a dark background. To get the bird in such a position may require considerable maneuvering, and to accomplish this before the bird decides to move on to some new place or position requires patience. This is particularly true if there are several people in the party of bird observers, all of them desiring to see the bird well in all its natural colors and markings. The lone observer, or at most a group of two or three, will always do better than a larger group. Yet people will insist on going into the field in large groups, and the teacher of field classes will necessarily have such problems with which to contend.

In maneuvering to get the bird into the best possible position for observation, it is well to bear in mind that slow, natural movements are best. Observers must restrain natural impatience. The bird will be less likely to fly away or drop out of sight into some thick cover if we take time with our movements. Quick, sudden movements, especially in the direction of the bird, are more likely to frighten it away than loud noise. Quiet conversation among observers may often be carried on without unfavorable results. One may better indicate the position of a bird to his friend by speaking than by pointing. One member of a group who persists in pointing will spoil many chances of the whole group to see birds well. In a large group it is almost certain that one or more members will be unable to control quick, sudden movements or refrain from pointing.

I have long believed that the ears of our smaller songbirds hear low-pitched sounds either with difficulty or not at all. The sounds they make are high-pitched, some even higher than the human ear can hear. It may be true that they do not hear low conversation of people at all, or that the voices of men, being an octave lower, are less perceptible to them than the voices of women.

There are reasons other than frightening the bird why observers should be quiet in the field. The presence of a particular, desirable bird is often first detected by the sound it makes. Such sounds, which are likely to be rather faint, will be overlooked when other noises distract attention from them.

There are many ways in which observers may manage to get into favorable positions to see birds. One of these is by sitting and quietly waiting in a favorable spot, where light conditions are picked beforehand to be good. I know a number of places where one may sit on a hillside or the top of a rock, with the sun at his back, and look into the tops of forest trees. Such a position, on a morning in the May migration, is wonderfully productive of results. I have sometimes found such places particularly good from which to watch the fall migration in August or September.

Birds that inhabit marshes and hide in the dense vegetation, such as rails and bitterns, are best observed by this method of waiting. I am reminded of a certain spot where a railroad track crosses a cattail marsh. If one walks along the track, he may see one or two frightened birds flying away at his approach. But if he sits down on the embankment in a favorable spot, where a view of open water surrounded by cattail growth is to be obtained, and waits patiently a half hour or so, he is likely to be rewarded with close observation of many marsh birds that he did not know existed in such a place.

Another favorite method that can be used on a beach is to sit in a favorable position with an incoming tide. The gulls, terns, or shore birds are far out on the edge of the water and difficult to distinguish, but as the tide comes in, the water line gets nearer and nearer till, if the observer is quiet, the birds are almost at his feet. Under such conditions little or no motion is essential to success. Birds pay little attention to a man who is still. If the observer can conceal himself in natural vegetation or a blind, results may be better, but, except for work around a nest, or bird photography, or in watching some especially wary species, concealment is by no means necessary.

An automobile is exceedingly useful in bird hunting. It has, however, both advantages and disadvantages. One may cover much more ground and reach distant places where especially desirable birds are to be found. There are often situations where one may stop a car along the edge of a pond, marsh, or seashore and observe water birds from the car. Birds are often less suspicious of a car than of a man on foot. I know of a number of cases where birds remained in full view from a car until one of the occupants got out. Then they flew immediately. Along a seashore or lakeside, where water birds are some distance away, one may use a telescope, running the car window down to the most convenient height to rest the telescope, and identify birds that could not have been distinguished with a smaller glass.

For finding land birds a car is chiefly serviceable in getting to the locality. But the birds are more successfully found on foot. It is often a good plan to have a circuitous route of roads or paths to follow through good bird territory, leading from the parked car and back to it. When good territory is near at hand, no car is necessary or desirable. In early mornings of May, when birds are singing abundantly, one may drive slowly along favorable country roads with the windows open and, if one knows songs, list birds by ear, stopping whenever a species one desires to see is heard, or to verify a song that is possibly doubtful. A car makes a certain amount of noise, however, that may keep some birds from being heard, and it may be desirable to stop in some favorable locality, turn off the engine, and listen. This sort of birding cannot be done on highways where there is considerable traffic, but on back-country roads early in the morning there are often no other cars around. I know some places where there is just enough downgrade so that I can remove my foot from the accelerator and let the engine idle, and thus travel a mile or more at a very low speed and with very little noise to drown the bird song.

The careful observation of a bird that is necessary for its identification by no means comes easily to everyone but usually requires training. One must observe not only the conspicuous colors and markings but also the duller ones. One must know the parts of a bird well enough to distinguish between throat and breast, sides and wings, and other such similar parts. One must distinguish among gray, brown, olive, and similar shades, particularly with the duller species. One must watch for those less conspicuous markings, wing bars, lines on heads, rings around eyes, stripes, bars, spots, and mottlings. Frequently the identification of a bird will rest on some obscure, dull marking, and if we cannot make it out our bird goes unnamed.

Of course an easy way to name the birds seen is to accompany someone who already knows and will oblige us by telling the names. If the chief object in view is a long list of the names of birds we have seen, this is an easy method. But if our object is really to know birds, to become an ornithologist, we will do better to work out our problems alone or to seek the company of that expert who will help us to find the bird and observe the significant things but will leave the correct naming of it to us. Once we have named the bird by our own observation, we will know and remember it better than if we obtained the name by some easier method. But we must not assume that we no longer need to observe that particular bird. We must see it again and again under many different conditions, not only till we know its colors and markings, but till each flit of its wing or twitch of its tail has become familiar. Then we find that it has become an old friend, and we, too, like the expert, name it at a glance, at such a distance that not a color or mark can be seen. Yet, through long familiarity, we know that our identification is right.

IDENTIFICATION BY SIZE.

The size of a bird is often a character that is of great help in its identification. In a number of cases certain species are chiefly different from each other in size, so far as field characters go. Size, including that of the bill, is the character that most commonly separates the downy and hairy woodpeckers, and the greater and lesser yellowlegs. It is important in distinguishing gulls and numbers of other birds.

But the size of a wild bird is not easily judged by one who is not used to it. If you do not already know, ask yourself how long a robin is from the tip of its bill to the tip of its tail. I have tried this question on individuals and classes many times, and the great majority underestimate the length from 20 to 40 per cent or more. Because of this tendency the sizes of birds expressed in inches mean less than sizes expressed as comparisons. That is, to say that a certain bird is a little larger than an English sparrow means more than to say that it is seven inches long.

Because man and domestic animals vary greatly in size between the largest and smallest individuals, people not familiar with wild birds and animals expect them to vary also. Of course there is some variation, but it is not great. With fish, reptiles, and other cold-blooded animals whose growths are indeterminate, there is great variation, making the "fish story," as to size, more or less plausible. But birds vary very little, and when they seem unusually large or small it is likely to be due to the conditions under which we see them rather than to an unusual size. When we hear stories of unusually large hawks, eagles, or other big birds, the figures given half again as large as the species grows, we know definitely that this is an exaggeration. In attempting to estimate sizes of birds we should not fall into such errors.

Young birds grow very rapidly and in the case of most of our songbirds are practically full grown when they leave the nest. While with some birds, such as grouse and ducks, we may see young birds that are distinctly smaller than the parents, this is only so for a little while, in the summer. A bird seen during any other season, one that is distinctly smaller than the rest of the kind it appears to be, is probably a different species.

Apparent size of a bird in the field seems to vary with the question of whether the bird is seen in flight or perching. This is particularly true of a bird with unusually long wings. Such a bird as the killdeer looks small on the ground but large in flight, whereas a short-winged bird, such as the meadowlark, gives a smaller impression when in flight than is the case.

When two species are much alike and differ chiefly in size, such as the common and fish crows and the herring and ring-billed gulls, the difference in size is not great enough to be used in identification unless the two species are near each other and can be compared. Even then the difference is not very apparent when the birds are in flight.

Judgment of the size of a bird is better made when the bird is near some object the size of which is known. When birds are seen in flight against an empty sky or over water or prairie, the lack of objects for comparison and the difficulty of judging distances are such that size characters are of little value.

IDENTIFICATION BY SHAPE

Birds, in general, are more nearly the same shape than most groups of animal life. But shapes differ in detail and are often exceedingly valuable in field identification. Frequently the beginner is so engrossed with colors and markings that he neglects to notice shape and cannot tell whether a certain bird seen had a short, stout bill or a long, slender one. Or he is not sure whether it had a long tail or a short one. Such characters are often the deciding factor in naming the bird. Yet shapes are so characteristic that many birds can be named by shape alone, or by shape combined with posture or habit of movement.

25

Factors that determine differences in shape are chiefly length of wing, tail, legs, neck, or bill, or the shapes of these parts. The shapes of bodies are not very different. The presence of a crest on the head and the shape of that crest are characters that are usually conspicuous and diagnostic. Shapes of heads when not crested often differ, especially in larger birds.

The shape of the body, whether round and plump, or slender, is often a variable character, because it is chiefly caused by the way the bird holds its feathers. In cold weather the feathers are erected and fluffed out, so that the body appears plump. The same kind of bird will appear slender in hot weather. I have known students who, seeing their first summer chickadee, could hardly be convinced that it was the same bird they knew so well in winter.

In addition to markings and size, the observer should note shape of the bill, whether long and slender or short and stout, whether straight or curved or hooked at the tip; shape of wings, whether rounded or pointed, narrow or broad; shape of the tail, whether rounded, square, emarginate, or forked. Length of legs and often their color are points worth noting and likely to be overlooked except in conspicuous cases.

Hawks are most commonly seen against the sky, where colors and markings are difficult to make out. Shape, combined with method of flight, is a character that gives a clue to the species. But this character is often the same in species of the same genus. Here is a place where the field observer needs to know something of classification and which hawks are Accipiters, which Buteos, and which Falcos. Buteos have long wings and a short tail, rounded at the end and spread like a fan when the bird is

Greater yellowlegs

in soaring flight. Accipiters have short wings and a long tail, the latter not commonly spread, for these hawks rarely soar. Falcos have long, sharp-pointed wings and a long tail. The marsh hawk, the osprey, and the eagles, which do not belong to any of these groups, have other characters that make their identification easy.

IDENTIFICATION BY HABIT AND POSTURE

A great many birds have certain habits of movement or postures in perching that are characteristic. Some of these will place the bird in a family or genus. Others are definitely characteristic of a particular species. Thus the constant restless motion of a small bird makes it probably a warbler, but a certain definite, rhythmic tail twitching makes it almost certainly a palm warbler. A robin-shaped brown bird alights on a limb and perches quietly. It is probably a thrush. But if we see the tail slowly rise to a position above the horizontal and then sink again, it is almost certainly a hermit thrush.

Such movements or actions are things to be noted. As they become more familiar they aid greatly in identification. I do not mean that one should rely on such actions alone as certain identification, particularly if he is not familiar with them. One of my students remarked, "But I saw a warbler twitch its tail, and it wasn't a palm warbler, but a myrtle warbler." Certainly! Other warblers twitch their tails; but the palm warbler's peculiar, more or less constant and rhythmic way of doing it is highly characteristic of that species alone. But one must become familiar with it to appreciate it.

The student should note and learn which kinds of water birds curl their necks when flying and which stretch them out in front; which kinds of birds walk on the ground and which hop; which birds soar when flying and which flap their wings, and so on, with numerous other habits. In most cases such habits as these are general, usually to be expected, but not without exception. Thus a great blue heron flies with the neck curled and the head resting back against the shoulders. But this is only after it is well launched into the air. As the heron rises into the air the neck is at first stretched out and is gradually curled back as the bird gets into extended flight.

In addition to becoming familiar with these habits and postures in the field, the student can get much from the photographs of living birds. Today photographs of birds are common, and there are few North American species that have not been photographed. While no one book contains photographs of a large number of species, if one searches through both books and ornithological magazines, he will find many. These photographs give the student a good idea of what each kind of bird looks like in the field. I believe that a good many field students have, perhaps unconsciously, come to know birds better through looking at photographs. The student who has access to back numbers of these magazines will find them worth while perusing. *Bird-Lore,* for example, published bird photographs for over forty years, and the total number of species represented must be considerable.

To a lesser extent drawings and paintings of birds may serve this same purpose, but in these so much depends on the artist and the extent to which his drawings are lifelike that not all

D. D'Aribo

Kingfisher hovering

Turnstone living up to its name

of them are to be recommended. A painting of a bird can be highly artistic and yet not look much like the live bird it is supposed to represent. But there are today in America bird artists, constantly increasing in number, who are following in the footsteps of Louis Fuertes and producing, like him, drawings and paintings that are both artistic and true to the field characters of living birds.

IDENTIFICATION BY HABITAT

Each kind of bird has a particular sort of place in which to live. While birds are able to fly about and appear almost anywhere, they nevertheless generally remain in particular localities, especially in summer when they are nesting. We do not expect to find bobolinks and meadowlarks in the woods, or thrushes and ovenbirds in open places. In the migration, birds sometimes appear in unexpected places, but even then such an occurrence is not common. So the knowledge of habitats chosen by particular birds is an aid in field identification.

In finding different kinds of birds we get better results by visiting a variety of habitats. I think of one particular bird sanctuary that has such a reputation that many people seem to think it is the only place to find birds in that vicinity. But that sanctuary is chiefly thicket. It contains no open fields, and while there are a number of large trees it contains no true forest areas. Therefore, certain kinds of birds are never found there, and those people who go there only are unaware that certain birds they have never seen are to be found easily only a short distance away.

33

IDENTIFICATION BY SONGS AND CALLS

Each kind of bird has songs or calls that are distinctive. The sound says definitely what kind of a bird makes it, and if we know that sound we may identify that bird, under normal conditions, as accurately by this means as by color, shape, or size. As a further advantage we do not, in such a case, have to see the bird at all. It makes no difference which way the light is shining or how many leaves or branches are between us and the bird. The bird deliberately says its name for everyone to hear.

This makes an easy method of identifying birds once one knows the songs or calls, but there are some uncertainties and some difficulties to overcome. Individual observers differ greatly in their ability to hear sounds and to distinguish the differences that are there. The songs of most of our birds are very high-pitched, and some people's ears are not attuned to hear these high pitches. Others who can hear them perhaps do not hear the overtones that give them a distinctive quality. Other people lack a sense of rhythm or cannot tell the difference between notes that are high or low and those that are loud or soft. Thus an observer whose ear for these distinctions is imperfect is more or less handicapped in using this method of identification. One who has such troubles in hearing songs cannot do anything about it. But there are many who simply do not notice songs and their differences merely because they have not paid attention to them. I am thinking of a man who was fond of birds

A singing wood thrush

and was very familiar with certain woodlands where scarlet tanagers were common breeding birds. Having seen only a few of them, he considered them rare. When in those same woodlands I called his attention to the song of the tanager, he remarked, "Why, I've heard that sound all my life and never knew what it was before."

One who has a good ear but has paid little attention to songs can better the matter by training and will soon realize that he finds many more birds than he could by sight alone. If one is to be a field ornithologist he should, if possible, learn to know and recognize songs and calls, for the observer who knows them is exceedingly more efficient in finding birds or watching the migration than one who does not. Nearly everyone can learn to hear and know at least some of the more conspicuous and distinctive bird sounds.

In some of the duller-colored groups of birds, where a number of species are much alike and require careful observation to distinguish by color, such as the thrushes and the small flycatchers, the songs and calls are much more distinctive than the plumage. I would hesitate to distinguish alder and least flycatchers by plumage except under extremely good conditions, but their call notes distinguish them immediately.

Some call notes, however, such as the "tsicks" of the warblers, are very much alike in the different species. But these birds are very distinct in their plumage, and their songs are distinct, even if their call notes are not. The different species of terns are more easily separated by their calls than by their plumages. The least and semipalmated sandpipers, which look so much alike, have different calls, and the greater and lesser yellowlegs are distinguished more certainly by their calls than by the rather doubtful difference in size.

So the observer who wishes to become efficient in field identification should pay particular attention to songs and calls. The observer who knows songs will find, when he visits a new region, that he can pick out the birds that will prove new by the new songs that he hears.

It is an interesting pastime for bird lovers to keep a life list of the species of birds they have seen. But such a list is not necessarily a measure of the ability of the observer. It may be a measure of the opportunities he has had to travel to many different localities. One might keep lists of other matters; for example, how large is the list of birds whose songs or call notes are so well known that you can identify a bird by them without seeing it?

THE QUESTION OF SUBSPECIES

Observers of wild birds in the field are often worried about the matter of subspecies. The most recent treatment to date, in the American Ornithologists' Union Check List, seems to put the subspecies almost on a par with the species, as it gives no definite name to the species as a whole, but does for each subspecies. The average bird lover seems to lack an understanding of just what a subspecies is and worries lest he should be naming a subspecies wrongly or missing one that he ought to see. To the evolutionist, subspecies are of considerable importance, but to the field student who identifies birds by sight only, they are of less value. From his standpoint they are not two different kinds of birds. The characters that separate two subspecies of the same species are usually minute: a slight difference in the shade of coloring of the back or breast, or a slight average difference in measurements. These characters usually cannot be determined definitely in the field. Even with specimens in the laboratory two different authorities on the subject will differ in their determination of a particular specimen.

What we should understand about subspecies is that they are separated geographically in their breeding ranges. In a given region there can be only one breeding subspecies. If the observer happens to live, however, in a place that is on the borderline between the breeding ranges of two different subspecies, the birds in his locality are liable to be intergrades and be more or less intermediate in character between the two forms. Individuals of the same subspecies sometimes vary as much as two different subspecies, and it is not uncommon to find an individual in the range of one subspecies that has the characters of another. In such cases we consider that the bird is merely an individual variant.

As a rule, two different subspecies of the same species do not differ from each other in habits, nesting, and only slightly or minutely in call notes, songs, or other field characters. On the other hand, two different species in the same genus definitely do differ in these things. In winter and during migrations two subspecies of the same species may occur together. In some cases, when examined carefully in good light, the subspecies can be distinguished. Hepburn and gray-crowned rosy finches, when in winter flocks on the Western prairies, can be distinguished easily by the extent of gray coloring on the head. Prairie and northern horned larks can be distinguished when seen closely on the ground, but if a flock is merely seen flying over, the characteristic flight and call notes will name them as horned larks, but nothing more.

The field student who thinks he can distinguish subspecies in the field should go to some good collection and examine skins and see how many different subspecies he can name correctly without looking at the labels. I believe that after such an experience he will be content to write song sparrow, fox sparrow, yellowthroat, etc., on his list and leave out the adjective that leads us to suppose that the subspecies were definitely determined. In publications concerning the habits of live birds, where identifications were made by sight only, it is best to do just this. Others can infer the subspecies observed from the locality just as readily as the writer, and it is quite possible that a new check list, or another supplement to it, may at any time declare the subspecies to be something different from what it was supposed to be.

For those who care to know more of birds than just their names, who may desire to become ornithologists and make some contributions to the science, identification is only the beginning. When one reaches the point where he knows all, or nearly all the birds that occur commonly in his region; when there are few new birds left to see, he need not go to another region where there will be new birds, nor need he decide that the thrills of bird study are all gone. There remain a large number of fields for study, a quantity of facts concerning birds and their lives that we do not know and that we are waiting for someone to discover. The discovery of these, even about the commonest and best-known birds, will give new thrills and new joys. By learning to identify birds, the student has taken the first step. Now he is ready to go on to serious study, to become a field ornithologist.

Keeping Notes and Records

THE beginning bird student soon becomes sufficiently interested to write down a list of the birds he has seen. He may add to this the dates on which he saw the first one of each species. But if his records are to be of value to the science of ornithology, he will go much farther than this. He will keep systematic notes of all the birds he sees on every field trip. If he lives where birds are to be observed daily, he keeps daily notes, whether he goes on a field trip or not.

Memory is a treacherous thing and not to be trusted. Young people usually have good memories, but that very fact leads them to trust memory too much. For years I have been attempting to teach high school boys and girls how to take notes. A boy comes to me to learn why his notebook mark was not so good as he thought it should be. I point out some of its discrepancies, and he replies, "But I didn't have to take notes about that. I remembered it." Then I remind him that when I asked a question about it on a recent test his memory was not so good.

It is probable that our memories of things that interest us deeply are better than they are of things we care little about. In fact, it would seem that we remember things of great interest without the least conscious effort to do so. But in other cases, where the material is not of great interest, we may make a systematic effort to remember the facts, and yet fail to do so for any great length of time. Even when an event occurs that is of great interest, we may remember the event, but forget the details. Much of scientific observation is a matter of details, details that are often, from the standpoint of science, of great importance. The study of live birds is full of such details, and though we think we will remember them, we should make a habit of writing them down at the first opportunity.

Methods of taking notes and filing them away in permanent form for later reference vary greatly, depending on the phase of bird life to which the notes pertain. I have suggested making a daily record of all the birds seen. It is rather laborious to write down a list of bird names each day. Other methods are in use, however, that shorten the labor. Field cards are issued with printed bird names and a place to check the species seen. My objection to such cards is that no printed list can fit a particular locality or season of the year unless it is an extremely large one, which means a lot of waste space. For a good many years I have used notebooks for daily records that are arranged by the month. The book has horizontal lines across each page, each line for one species. At the left is a space for the name of the bird, and the rest of the page is divided, by vertical lines, into thirty-one spaces for the thirty-one days of a full month. I write the names of the birds as I see them and then check off in the spaces for each day they are seen. The space for each day is large enough to include a number, for the number of individuals seen, and other letters or marks pertaining to some special observation. Thus, an "s" over the check mark means that the bird was heard singing that day, and aids me in keeping track of song periods. Other letters, such as "n.b.," "n.4e.," or "n.3y.," indicate "nest building," "nest and four eggs," or "nest and three young." A book ruled in this manner is commonly sold in stationery stores under the name of "monthly time book." It is designed to keep the time of workmen who are paid by the month, but it serves fairly well for a bird record. If there were enough call for it, I presume such a book might be published and sold especially for bird students.

One may question the value of keeping a record of daily occurrence of such a common bird as the robin, for example. After its spring migration it is recorded practically every day. But it is hard to say just where to draw the line. In every month some species occur that are important to record, and daily records give some idea of the relative abundance of a species. In my record book for the year 1938, for example, I find the robin recorded every day from March 24 to September 6. This is good testimony to the abundance of this bird, for the notes are not all from one locality but include observations in six different states. In the month of June for that same year I find the hooded warbler recorded only six times, and the Louisiana water thrush four times, indicating the much smaller numbers and local distribution of those species.

Daily records will show not only when migratory species arrive, but when they become common enough to be seen every day, and when the last ones depart. In the fall it is the only way to be sure when you saw the last one of a summer-resident species.

How we keep other records than those of daily occurrence of birds depends on what the notes are about. For nests I prefer a loose-leaf notebook, with a separate page or pages for each nest under observation. One carries such a notebook in the field and records on the spot just what takes place at the nest on each visit. If a nest has a page allotted to it, and then is broken up by some enemy at the very next visit, so that the page has almost nothing on it, it should be saved, nevertheless, and the cause of the failure of the nest recorded, if known. Such notes contribute to knowledge of the percentage of nests that fail and why they fail. Notebook sheets on nests or other subjects should be filed away in some systematic manner so they can be found when needed. One may keep them in alphabetical order, if he prefers. Personally I prefer to keep mine in the order of the American Ornithologists' Union Check List.

In addition to the daily record one should keep a general record of field trips, recording the weather conditions and just where the trip took place, who else, if anyone, was along, and how many hours were spent in the field. Such notes prove to be valuable when one goes over notes of some years back and questions come up about just where and under what conditions a certain observation was made.

Watching the Migration

THE lives of birds are greatly influenced by the season of the year. When one keeps track of the dates on which he sees certain birds, he soon finds that his lists have some significance in determining the season when certain birds occur. The beginning bird student is likely to make his first observations in the spring, when birds are migrating, and soon the fact of migration impresses itself on him.

Observations on migration have been made for many years, but we still have much to learn about the subject. To a very large extent the study of migration is one for the field student. We can, of course, gain some knowledge of migration by examining the dates on specimens in the museum. But to get all the data we need would require too many specimens. For the fullest and most complete data we must rely on field observation.

Anyone with a good knowledge of the birds of his region can

contribute something to our knowledge of migration from his observations. But to do thorough work on the migration each year requires being out in the field practically every day through the season. If we are observing only once a week, we may miss much that goes on. The great wave of migration that is likely to come in most localities may not occur on the day we are in the field. A number of species may make their arrival or departure on a day when we are not looking for them. Even when we are observing every day we may miss something. Certain species will be seen a day or two earlier by someone else, no matter how constantly we are on the watch.

The matter is not merely one of determining the first day on which a species arrives, but much more. When a species was first noted, was only one individual or several observed? Did it increase in numbers the next day, or several days later? Were all the first arrivals males? If so, how soon did the females come? If it is a breeding bird in your region, does it occur in migration in places other than where it breeds, or only in the breeding localities? If a transient species, when does it begin to decrease and when was it last seen? How does the weather affect migration? Do birds arrive on warm nights or cold nights? Is this the same in both spring and fall? Does wind affect migration? Do individuals of transient species stay several days or go on immediately?

The greater part of migration takes place at night. This is especially true of the smaller land birds. What we observe chiefly is the birds that have arrived. With the beginning of daylight they drop down into the bushes and trees to feed. For a few hours they are active and, in spring, singing, and are easily found. Later in the day they become quieter. The observer who waits till nine o'clock in the morning or till afternoon to go looking for birds will find comparatively few. This is true of bird observation at all times, but particularly so in studying migration.

I realize that the study of birds is, to most of us, an avocation, not a vocation, and that therefore such a study of migration as I have suggested, requiring field work every day, seems impossible. Most of us must earn a living and be at the store or office or shop at 8 or 9 A.M. five or six days a week. Only the week ends seem available for bird study. This is a handicap in the study of fall migration, but really not so much so in spring, for there are several hours of daylight between dawn and eight o'clock, and they are the best hours of the day to watch bird migration. Even when people save one of these hours by daylight-saving time, there are still several more that the bird lover can save, hours when few people are abroad to stare curiously at the man with bird glasses, and when there is little traffic on the roads to disturb the observer and drown out the bird songs.

It is not our work that we must sacrifice in order to study bird migration, but social affairs that keep us up too late in the evenings to permit rising before sunrise. The real bird student, who knows the joy of watching the spring migration through in the early mornings, is willing to sacrifice evenings to do this. For forty years I have rarely missed an early morning in the months of April and May. Yet I, too, have had work to do, work that required my presence soon after 8 A.M. and took one more hour away when daylight saving came in.

Actual migration at night can be observed by watching birds

cross the disk of the moon with a glass. But species cannot be definitely determined at such times. One may also observe night migration by ear, and hear the sounds of birds passing over. The sounds, however, seem to be different from the ones used in daytime, and most of them are unrecognizable, though at times these sounds may be heard by daylight and the species that makes them determined.

Some migration can be seen in the daytime, such as the flights of hawks along the tops of mountain ridges in the fall. Flocks of water and shore birds often migrate by day, and the same is true of swallows. If one is out before actual daylight he may hear or see birds come in. Once, in Montana, I watched a group of kingbirds do this. I first heard the sharp, high-pitched rasping cries of the birds, high up and far away. Then I watched them, one by one, drop down from a great height to the tops of the cottonwood trees.

Notes on weather conditions and how they affect migration are very worth while. When one has observed migration through a period of years, he finds surprising differences from year to year. Not only are the seasons early in some years and late in others, but some begin by being early but become late before the migration has ceased. Others are late at the beginning and early at the end. The popular superstition that birds know what the weather is to be and are indicators of an early or a late spring has no basis in fact. When the March migrants appear in the latter half of February, it indicates only that the season is early at the time. It is no indication of what May will be.

After two or three years of experience observers often think that they know pretty well just when each species will arrive. But it takes longer experience than that to know all the vagaries of migration seasons. Even after long experience one finds that his impressions are faulty. He remembers early arrivals and forgets late ones. Some years ago, after accumulating some twenty years of migration dates in my locality, I began averaging the dates. I was greatly surprised to find one species after another averaging later than I supposed. Here was a bird that I figured must arrive by May 1 at the latest. I had often seen the first ones in April. Yet when I averaged all the dates, it came out May 4. I had forgotten those late years; those times when the first week of May was still mid-April as far as weather and temperature were concerned.

There are evidently cycles of early and late years; several years together when birds arrive early, followed by several more years of late arrivals. If one begins his study of migration in a period of early years, he gets a wrong impression of what the average year is like. The whole question of the relation of migration to various weather conditions is still none too well known. Light, temperature, humidity, wind, all have their effects. These conditions, in turn, are evidently influenced by the occurrence of sunspots, but it is still not apparent that the occurrence of early and late years of migration follows the regular cycles of sunspots.

Much has been said and noted about the sudden heavy storms that cause birds to occur in localities where they are not commonly found, but there still remains much to be learned about more normal conditions. Keeping a record of weather conditions from day to day is of value, but we must remember that local weather conditions are of less importance in such a phenomenon as migration than general weather conditions over a large part of the country, particularly southward and northward. The records of the weather bureaus over the whole country will probably prove of greater value than local records.

There is often much said about a correlation between the arrival of birds in spring and the development of vegetation; the blossoming of certain flowers, or the development of foliage on trees. One of my friends remarked that the orioles arrive when the cherry trees bloom. But I have noted several years in which cherry trees are in full bloom several days to a week or more before the first orioles come. The point is that the development of plants in any given region is determined only by the local weather conditions, whereas the migration of birds depends upon weather in other regions also. Unfavorable weather conditions south of the particular locality where we are observing may hold up migration, when the weather we are experiencing is entirely favorable and causes plants to leaf out or bloom at comparatively early dates.

In the year of 1946 we had an unusually good example of this. Unseasonably warm weather in March brought out leaves and flowers very early, but birds were not noticeably earlier than usual. When May and the warbler migration arrived, the leaves were already out, and the foliage was so dense that the birds were hard to find. The oak blossoms, with which many of us associate the warblers, were already gone by. In 1947 the reverse of this was true. The birds were about on time, but the vegetation was slow in developing. A heavy flight of warblers appeared, and, because of the slight foliage, opportunities to observe them were exceptionally good.

The question of food supply while birds are on migration is an important one. When development of plants has some relation to this, it may have much to do with the arrival of birds or their lingering in a particular locality. Ducks move northward when the weather is warm enough to melt the ice on the ponds, lakes, and marshes where they feed. But the birds do not actually know that the ice is gone. They merely move northward with warmer weather, and if they find colder weather and icebound water northward, they are likely to return southward for a time. It is quite probable that retrogressive migration takes place in spring quite frequently, but we have comparatively few notes on the subject.

Along our beaches there is a small fly that breeds in decaying seaweed. Adults of this fly are likely to be on the wing on warmer days in every month of the year. In spring they are likely to be quite abundant, though the weather is still cold and flying insects elsewhere are scarce. Under such conditions in April it is not uncommon to see flocks of migrating swallows following the beach in a northward direction and capturing these flies as they go. The flies sit on the sand and fly low, only an inch of so above it, when disturbed. I have frequently seen the swallows brush their breasts against the sand when capturing these insects.

These are a few examples of things that may be noted about migration. There are undoubtedly many more such facts waiting for some observant bird student to note and put on record. Even when the fact observed has been seen and recorded by someone else, it is still worth noting. Corroboration of another's observation is always worth while and tends to show to what extent the occurrence is widespread and common.

Fall migration is less well known than that of spring. It is more difficult to observe for several reasons. Birds are harder to find and identify than in spring. Many are in duller plumages or the lesser-known juvenile and immature plumages. There is little singing at that season, some species not singing at all, and others only rarely. In the earlier part of the fall, when the migration is actually at its height, the leaves on the trees are still thick and have not begun to fall, so that birds are hard to observe. There are fewer hours of daylight in which to make observations, and those who have other work to do have no time either before or after working hours in which to make observations. Those who can find the time to watch the fall migration will find that it will test their enthusiasm, patience, and powers of observation to the utmost. But the facts to be gained by such observation should be particularly worth while.

In a general way fall migration is a reverse of that of spring, but it is by no means perfectly so. Species do not depart in the reverse of the order in spring; that order is changed about in many particulars. While the robin and bluebird come early and go late, and the indigo bunting comes late and goes early, there are other species, the Louisiana water thrush, for example, that come early and go early, and others, such as the blackpoll warbler, that come late and go late. The fall migration lasts longer than in spring. In northern United States it begins in July and lasts to at least December, and I have often had reason to believe that it is not entirely over till the middle of January. Very cold weather and deep snows are often delayed till the middle of January. There are certainly more species and individuals present in December than in late January. Along the coast there are some winters when the coastal waters freeze over in midwinter, and the ducks that were present disappear. It isn't reasonable to suppose that they all die or that they go any other direction than south, and, while the movement may be short, it is nevertheless, in my opinion, right to call it the last part of fall migration.

Certain experiments have shown that the increase and decrease of light with the changes of season are compelling factors in causing migration. Some have gone so far as to suppose that all migration in fall is southward until December 21 and northward thereafter. There seems nothing more to prove this than that decrease of light does affect migration. But when decrease of heat, which in eastern United States is greater after December 21, causes conditions under which birds cannot get food, then that seems, for the time being at least, more important than light.

This brings us to the question of just what causes birds to go north in spring and south in fall, instead of some other direction. If birds go north as sunlight increases, even though weather conditions still make living conditions impossible, many must perish. These would have no descendants, whereas individuals that continued to move southward and could find food and favorable living conditions would have descendants. These would be inclined to inherit the tendency to go south because of cold, rather than north because of light. In other words, birds migrate in the right direction and to the proper place by instinct, inherited from a long line of ancestors that survived because they migrated in the right direction. A selective process has picked out the individuals with the proper migration instincts since the days when migration first became necessary. I do not doubt the importance of the influence of light on migration, but I do doubt that it is the sole factor. Only a small remnant of birds would survive if their migratory instincts were influenced by light alone.

The student, however, should make his own observations in the field, read what others have had to say on the subject, and form his own opinions. When questions are theoretical, there are bound to be differences of opinion. The more we can learn about the migrations of wild birds under natural conditions, the nearer we will come to knowing the whole truth.

The observer of migration in one locality can learn much, but many of the facts we want to know can be obtained only by many observers in different localities. The spirit of cooperation necessary in all fields of scientific endeavor is particularly necessary in the study of bird migration.

Because of migration the birds that occur in any one region may be divided into groups, according to their seasonal occurrence. Some species do not migrate, or if some individuals do, there are nevertheless individuals present throughout the year. These are known as residents. Other species are present in summer, in the breeding season, but migrate to some place farther south for the winter. These are summer residents. Other species breed entirely north of the region but come south in the fall and remain for the winter. These are winter visitors.

Some people call them winter residents, but I prefer to use the term "resident" only for species that breed in the region in question. Still others that breed farther north come south in the fall, but go on farther south for the winter. In the same manner they go through again in spring in the opposite direction. These are transients.

Some transient species have a more or less circuitous route and may occur in a given region only or mainly in fall, or in spring, and not in the corresponding season. These are termed fall transients or spring transients, as the case may be. There is also a small class of sea birds that breed in the South Temperate or Antarctic zones in the season that is our winter and come north to spend the summer (their winter) with us. These may be termed summer visitors. This would also probably be the best term to use for those herons that spread north of their breeding ranges in late summer, after the nesting season is over.

When we come to classify the species of a region according to these seasonal occurrences, there appear some cases that are not in one class alone. Most of the song sparrows of New England are summer residents, but in southern New England, at least, a small number of individuals remain every winter and are residents. In other cases a species that is a regular summer resident may have a few wintering individuals once in a period of years, but not every year. In some regions certain species are common as transients and rare as either summer residents or winter visitors.

Since food is the important factor in the bird's life that makes migration necessary, even if light is the primary cause, there are sometimes winters when food of a certain kind is abundant and others when it is scarce. Because of this there are certain species that may be known as erratic winter visitors, appearing in certain southern localities once in a period of years, when their food supply farther north has failed. Most of these species are seed-eating finches, such as the pine grosbeak and the redpoll, but some are predatory birds, such as the snowy owl and the goshawk.

The Nesting Cycle

W HEN the spring migration is over and birds
have returned to their summer homes, nesting begins. Then
occurs a series of actions, evidently entirely or mainly instinctive, by which reproduction is accomplished. These actions
occur one after another, in a definite order, and thus constitute a cycle. The study of the nesting behavior of each species
of bird is of great importance to the science of ornithology.
There is much to learn, even about the commonest species.
In fact, the study of the nesting of some of our commonest birds
has been rather neglected in a number of cases, students perhaps supposing that the nesting of these common birds must
have been studied thoroughly, and therefore turning their attention to rarer species. The result is that some of our rarer
birds have been studied more thoroughly than the common
ones.

In the study of the various phases of nesting behavior there is a large field for the student of living birds. Although quite a number of students are now paying attention to this division of field ornithology, there is still plenty of opportunity to learn new facts. Even when a species has been studied over and over, new things come to light with each study, and the interest is far from gone. The study is fascinating. At the Allegany School of Natural History I found it common experience that students would start studying a bird's nest, expecting it to be tedious and wearing upon the patience, but when the experience was over they would bemoan the fact that the young birds grew up and left the nest and there was nothing more to watch.

In the first place, there are some misunderstandings concerning birds' nests on the part of the general public. Nests have been commonly referred to as "bird homes," but actually they are not homes, but cradles. We need a cradle, or whatever its modern substitute is, in our homes only when our children are very little. Birds need a nest only when they have eggs, or young that are small and helpless. The period of time when a bird has a nest which it uses is but a short part of the year. It is also at a very definite season. In the fall and winter, after the post-nuptial molt, birds lose their nesting and mating instincts and have no nests, no mates, and no family life. The nest is not a place to go to at night. Birds spend the night perched in a sheltered spot. When there are eggs or small young, the female sits on the nest at night, but not when the young are well grown. With some of the swallows, where the nest is larger, both male and female may be in the nest together, and the young return for some days after they can fly, but this is an exception. With the great majority of birds, when the young are old enough, they leave the nest, and neither they nor their parents return to it again.

A question that is frequently asked is, "Do birds that nest in the North in summer have another nest in the South when they go there for the winter?" This question illustrates a complete misunderstanding of the seasonal life of a bird. Since the nest has nothing to do with any part of a bird's life other than reproduction, there is no nest in winter, as there is no family life, no children, and no special distinctions between the sexes. In the winter each bird is living a simple life in which there are but two main requirements: food, and protection from enemies or other danger. It may live a solitary existence, or in flocks with others of its kind, according to what kind of bird it is. But a bird of the opposite sex is merely another bird and not considered as a possible mate. Birds are practically sexless in fall and winter, and since song is a phenomenon connected mainly with mating and nesting, it is a general rule that birds sing not at all or very little in those seasons. There are some exceptions to this, for some birds sing so constantly that they cannot keep quiet, even in fall and winter. But the species that sing much at that time are few.

Strictly speaking, the first step in the nesting cycle is spring migration, for the bird must get from its winter home to the locality where it is to nest. With the coming of spring and the increase of light, a physical change takes place in the bird. The sex organs begin to enlarge, and this is evidently what first impels spring migration. It has been shown that increase of ultraviolet light causes the physical change, but we are still uninformed as to what starts migration in birds that winter at the equator or south of it. Their migration may begin before the physical change takes place.

THE TERRITORY THEORY

When the birds arrive at their breeding grounds in the North, the second step is the selection of a particular breeding locality or territory. The first birds to arrive are usually males, and, as a general rule, it is the male that selects the locality where nesting is to take place. But in such a thing as bird behavior there seem always to be exceptions. The territory theory has served to help us understand the early phases of the nesting cycle. It has also served to make us inquire more critically into the matter, to determine to what extent each species has territory and follows the general rules. There have been criticisms of the theory, and there are undoubtedly cases where it does not apply in its ordinary interpretation, or applies only in part. In colonial nesters, territory is an altogether different thing, if it applies at all.

Briefly, the territory theory is as follows: The male bird selects a territory in which to breed. In this territory are one or more perches from which he sings. His song is loud, often repeated, and characteristic of the species to which he belongs. It serves to warn other males of his species to keep away, and he defends the territory if another male intrudes. The song also serves to notify female birds that he has a territory and desires a mate. When the mate arrives, and is definitely chosen, the

Field sparrow singing in his territory

song ceases and the nesting begins. Both birds thereafter will defend the territory against the encroachment of others.

With some species this theory fits nicely, but when we apply it to others we find all sorts of variations in the conditions. In some species the male does not arrive on the territory first, but the pair together. In others the male does not cease singing with the arrival of the mate, or does so for a time, but resumes singing when incubation begins. In fact, there are all sorts of variations in the application of the theory to different species, and much opportunity for the field student to discover facts and help us to a clearer understanding of the matter.

COURTSHIP

To return to the nesting cycle: the male selects the nesting locality in a majority of cases and sings from a point within the area. After a few days a female arrives and courtship begins. Comparatively little is known about courtship in the majority of birds. It is exceedingly brief and difficult to observe in most species. There may be special songs used only at such times, often accompanied by display, strutting, and dancing. In some game birds there are community dances, and it is hard to know what this has to do with selection of mates. In some species there is evidently rivalry between two or more males, but this is, theoretically at least, not when there is definite territory. Some ducks evidently court and choose mates in late winter and remain in pairs thereafter, migrating to the breeding grounds after mates are chosen. Yet courtship in these species also takes place on the breeding grounds, and courtship-like behavior may be observed at almost any season of the year. Questions have been raised as to selection of mates and how much sexual selection has to do with the evolution of bright plumages and finer songs in the males. Too often naturalists have sat indoors and theorized about such things, when what we need is close, careful observation in the field.

One point that makes a difference in nesting behavior is that of monogamy or polygamy. Most of our songbirds are monogamous; that is, they have but one mate at the time of nesting. Monogamy in birds, however, does not mean mating for life, for the mating relations break up at the end of the nesting season and are not resumed till the following spring, when it is not at all certain that the same two birds will be mated again. Banding of birds has shown that birds sometimes change mates between broods in the same nesting season. But the pair remain mated for a single nesting, so long as the young require parental care. In most cases where there is true polygamy the male has nothing to do with the nest or the care of the young. It would seem as though courtship performances and displays are more conspicuous and more easily observed in birds that are polygamous, but in some species the question of polygamy or monogamy is not easily determined.

NEST BUILDING

After mates are definitely chosen, the next step is nest building. It is probable that the female chooses the exact location of the nest, for in most cases she does most of the nest building and often all of it. But here again is a point where we have too little information. It is not always easy to find a nest just as it is being built and to watch it all through the cycle.

The location and structure of nests vary greatly, but the general notion that a bird's nest is up high in a tree is true only in a small number of cases. A majority of nests are either on the ground or a few feet above it. Many nests are in holes in trees or posts or poles. A few species nest in holes in banks or on rocky cliffs. Marsh birds often build in reeds, cattails, or other vegetation growing out of the water, while grebes make nests that actually float on the water, though attached to marsh vegetation.

Nests in trees are often better and more complicated structures than those on the ground. There is often little material in the structure of ground nests, but the finely woven nests of beautiful structure are those in trees, especially those that are pensile or semipensile. Tree nests may be supported in a crotch, hung from a branch, saddled on a limb, or placed against the trunk, supported by one or two projecting branches. Each species of birds has a particular sort of nesting site that it prefers, but there is often considerable variation in individuals of each species. The exact procedure in nest building in each species is not too well known, nor whether all individuals go about it in the same manner.

EGG LAYING

When the nest is finished, the eggs may be laid almost immediately or there may be a wait of a few days. When one finds an empty nest, if it does not show signs of having contained eggs or young, it is well to watch it for a few days before concluding that it is deserted. Eggs are generally laid in the early morning hours, one each day until the set is complete. The number of eggs varies from one to eighteen or twenty, varying in different kinds of birds. The majority of our smaller songbirds have from three to five.

All through the nesting cycle it seems apparent that each step of the cycle must be completed, must satisfy the instinct of the bird, before the next step is taken. Egg laying continues until the set is complete, and, according to experiments performed by some of our egg collectors in the past, if one egg is removed daily, leaving one as a nest egg, egg laying goes on indefinitely, the bird never reaching the next step, incubation, so long as the nest does not contain the full complement of eggs. Such experiments were carried on chiefly with the flicker, but it is undoubtedly the same sort of condition that induces the domestic hen to continue to lay one egg a day without attempting incubation. Evidently the mental condition of an unsatisfied instinct has a control over the physical one of producing eggs.

Evidently this same sort of condition can occur in the matter of nest building. I observed a case in which a flicker attempted to nest in the side of an icehouse, drilling a hole in the outside wall and removing the sawdust between the walls. But as soon as the hole was completed, the owner of the ice house nailed a sheet of tin over it. Before the summer was over, that icehouse was spotted on nearly all sides with pieces of tin, and

Incubating blue jay

the owner was resorting to flattened tin cans for material, firm in his resolve that he wouldn't let that bird nest in his icehouse.

There seem to be few cases on record that tell the definite time between coition and the laying of the first egg. It is probable that the period is short and that eggs are fertilized after they are partly developed, but before the shell is formed. It is not uncommon for eggs to be laid that are infertile. In some seasons, especially in second-brood nests, a majority of nests contain one or more infertile eggs. I knew of one case, with a cedar waxwing, where five eggs in a nest were incubated until after the young of other nests of that species in the near vicinity had raised their young. When the bird finally deserted the nest, the eggs all proved to be infertile. I believe that the bird in that case had no mate. The period between coition and egg laying may be longer in larger birds. In Connecticut, where laughing gulls are transient and there are no breeding colonies anywhere in the state to my knowledge, birds observed in late May are evidently mated, and coition frequently takes place.

INCUBATION

When the set of eggs is complete, incubation begins. Commonly the female bird performs this, but in a number of species the male takes his turn, and among some of the shore birds the male alone incubates. Watching a nest while incubation is in progress is a tedious matter compared to watching it when young are being fed. Consequently we know little about how closely birds sit on the nest; whether the male feeds his mate when she performs the duty; how often mates spell each other when both sexes share the duty; and how often eggs are turned or moved about.

The period of incubation varies in different species from ten days or less to thirty days or more. There are a good many species in which we do not know the period definitely, and others in which further corroboration would be of value. It is probable that the actual period varies more or less in different cases. If eggs were kept in an incubator at a definite even temperature, the period would probably be uniform, but under natural conditions some birds sit more constantly and closely than others. Eggs may cool off somewhat, the coolness not killing the embryos, but merely delaying the time of hatching. The hummingbird seems to be an example of a bird in which the period is exceedingly variable in different individuals because the birds vary greatly in the amount of time they actually spend in incubation. Ducks, when leaving the nest, cover the eggs with the down of which the nest is composed. Grebes, similarly, cover the eggs with the wet plant materials that compose the nest. It is my experience that woodpeckers, vireos, and some of the finches share the duty of incubation between the two sexes, so that the eggs are rarely uncovered for more than a short period. Probably some other birds have this habit, but much is still unknown on the subject.

Another question is just what causes the difference in the incubation period of different kinds of birds. Probably it is a combination of several factors. Small birds usually have a shorter period than large ones, and the temperature of small birds' bodies is greater than that of large ones. For that reason

Blue-headed vireos about to change places on the nest

the temperature of the bird was believed to be the main factor for some time. But other factors must be considered. Precocial young ones are more fully developed when hatched than altricial ones, and therefore should require a longer period. Yet the hawks, which are altricial, seem to have a longer period than some precocial birds of about equal size.

To determine the period of incubation, the usual procedure is to count the days from the laying of the last egg to the hatching of the eggs. But there are often twenty-four hours or more between the hatching of the first and last egg. In a number of non-passerine birds incubation often begins before the last egg is laid, and the laying of the last egg is often irregular. In such cases the young hatch at intervals and are not all of the same size or age.

CARE OF YOUNG

When the eggs hatch, care of the young begins. The kind and amount of care given the young vary, first of all with the question of whether they are altricial or precocial. When the young, at hatching, are like small chickens, well covered with down, eyes wide open, with ability to stand up and move around, they are precocial. When, like young songbirds, they are but sparsely covered with down, blind, unable to stand or do anything but lift the head and open their mouths for food, they are altricial. Such birds as ducks, grouse, and shore birds illustrate the highly precocial type, while songbirds and woodpeckers are extremely altricial. Herons are altricial, but their young have eyes open and are able to stand very soon after hatching. Gulls and terns are precocial, but quite dependent on the parents to bring them food for a long time after hatching. Young grouse seem able to pick up their food from the very first, and, so far as I know, are not fed by the parent. The same seems true of young ducks and sandpipers, but the young of gallinules and grebes, though able to swim immediately after hatching, are fed by the parents for a time.

Precocial young are found on the ground or on water until able to fly. Land forms, such as grouse, are able to fly before they are half grown. Young precocial birds are led about by the parent, and the latter protects them by calling a danger signal, at which the young hide expertly, often dropping still right where they are when their protective coloring is such that they are almost impossible to see. The parent, in such cases, often feigns injury, a habit common to many birds that have precocial young, and to some that are altricial, especially ground nesters.

This injury feigning has been a matter of considerable discussion. It often seems as though it were a case of reasoning on the part of the bird, but there is no ground for assuming reasoning, however much it appears to be such. That is, the habit is too common. Each species goes through the action in a way characteristic of that species. The habit can be accounted for as an instinct that perhaps first arose from a nervous action on the part of the parent, and, proving an aid in protection of the young, finally became a fixed, inherited habit.

In interpreting all sorts of habits of birds we should beware of assuming reasoning. While I am not entirely skeptical about

A wood duck, by feigning injury, saves its brood

reasoning on the part of birds to a limited extent, it is best not to assume it without sound grounds for doing so. If a bird should face some situation quite new to it, and meet that situation with some unusual action that could not be common to the species, that would be grounds for believing that the bird did some reasoning. But few, if any, such cases are known where there is not some element of doubt.

In the case of altricial young there are three main things that the parent bird must do: feed the young, protect them from heat, cold, rain, and enemies, and clean the nest. Feeding is of first importance. Birds have high body temperatures, rapid heart action and circulation, and rapid digestion, growth, and metabolism. Consequently they need large quantities of food. It is of prime importance that the parent bird should be able to obtain plenty of food within a reasonable distance of the nest. For most of our smaller birds the greater part of that food is insects. Anyone who has watched birds feeding young in a nest will marvel at the ability of the parents to obtain a billful of insects every few minutes. But it is necessary that they do so in order to raise a nestful of young, and if we did not have insects in abundance we could not have birds.

Often young birds are unable to digest food fed to them directly. Consequently, in such instances, parent birds swallow the food first and regurgitate it in a partly digested state to feed the young. Just which species feed young birds by regurgitation is imperfectly known. In some cases we can observe the fact with ease, but in many others it is difficult to know certainly whether regurgitation takes place or not. It has been claimed that all, or nearly all, songbirds regurgitate food when the young are very small, but the case does not seem to have been proved.

The exact character of food fed to the young is a difficult matter to make out. Many of our bird observers have no great knowledge of insects, and even when they do it is usually impossible to make certain identification of the insects in a bird's bill.

Foods, other than insects, that are commonly used among our smaller birds are earthworms, spiders, snails, berries or other fruits, and seeds. With larger birds, the birds of prey use mice, rabbits, birds, reptiles, fish, and large insects, while water birds, such as gulls, use almost any and every form of marine life. One who would study all the kinds of foods that birds eat must be an accomplished zoologist and botanist. But if we cannot identify with certainty the character of a bird's food, we can learn such things as how often birds are fed and how the rate of feeding varies at different times of day.

The gathering of sufficient food is such a task that usually both sexes take part in the feeding. Males that have had little or nothing to do with nest building and incubation not only feed the young, but in some cases do so more often than the female. It is not always possible to be sure which bird is the male and which the female. In many species there is no definite difference in plumage. But one soon learns to distinguish the two individual parents when watching a nest. There is individuality, and it may appear in the plumage or appearance, or else in habits, such as the manner or direction from which the bird approaches the nest. If one of the two birds sings, we normally expect that one to be the male, though there are some cases where female birds sing a little. But in many species singing ceases during the period of feeding young.

As mentioned above, when young altricial birds are newly hatched, about all they can do is lift their heads and open their mouths for food. With a good many birds that nest in bushes a slight movement of the bush is sufficient to cause each mouth to open. The young do not distinguish between the approach of a parent with food and that of an ornithologist making observations. But in hole-nesting birds, before their eyes are open, something else is evidently necessary to cause mouths to open. In the house wren, and perhaps all wrens, the stimulation that causes mouths to open is the song of the male. With the bluebird it is apparently the call note, the soft whistled "oo-ah-loo"; at least I have been able to cause mouths to open with an imitation of this note.

There are sometimes unusual things to be observed in the matter of feeding. Instincts to feed young are strong when developed, and some cases are known where a bird of one species will feed young of another, probably where its own young have met with a tragic end and the instinct to feed has not been entirely satisfied. With the Florida gallinule the young of the first brood, full grown but in immature plumage, have been seen to feed downy young of the second brood. This seems a rather human sort of proceeding, where older sister or brother helps to care for the younger children.

When young altricial birds are very small, they need less food and are fed less frequently. At the same time their bodies are rather sparsely covered with down, and they frequently need protection from cold, rain, or excessive heat. At such times parent birds spend more time in brooding than in feeding. Just how much time is spent in brooding and how that changes with development of the young are points on which we need more information. Even when young are well grown, parents sometimes protect them from rain or sunlight by standing above them with outstretched wings.

One case of protection of young that came to my attention seemed quite remarkable. I had found in a small spiraea bush an alder flycatcher's nest that contained a half-grown young bird and two infertile eggs. The nest was very poorly supported in the bush and was tipped to one side. In the middle of the night there came a thunderstorm with exceedingly heavy rain. The next morning I visited the nest at the first opportunity to see how it had fared. The nest, both eggs, and the young bird were on the ground, but the young bird was perfectly dry, healthy, and hungry. It looked as if the parent had found it in the middle of the night and brooded and protected it through the storm. I replaced the nest and its contents in a more secure situation, and the birds continued to feed and care for the young bird so that it left the nest successfully.

Protection of young from danger is sometimes the matter of injury feigning and sometimes a direct attack on the enemy. Many of the songbirds use direct attack rather than injury feigning. We may judge this from the behavior of the birds toward man, but many species that will attack other enemies do not attack man. There is also a considerable difference in individuals. When the nest contains young, the wood thrush will sometimes fly directly at the eyes of a man who comes too near. But another wood thrush, under similar circumstances,

A family of pied-billed grebes

will merely protest. Brown thrashers are equally variable, sometimes striking the head or neck of a man who bends over the nest. When their young have just left the nest, blue jays will often attack ferociously any man who innocently comes near the young. Both screech and barn owls will often attack people who happen to be near their young after dark. A male marsh hawk whose nest I was studying attacked me on every occasion, but the female never did. On the other hand, when I have climbed to nests of both red-shouldered and Swainson's hawks containing young, the parents never came near me.

Most birds do not attack until they are sure the nest has been discovered, but the kingbird attacks any larger bird that flies by, whether it comes near the nest or not. Yet I have never known a kingbird to attack a man. Most birds do not attack man, but merely protest at his presence by continual repetition of the alarm note. But such birds will attack natural enemies. I have seen juncos that paid no attention to a man near their nest and young make a furious attack on a chipmunk that chanced to run by. I have also seen them hopelessly attack a milk snake that swallowed some of their young.

Alarm notes serve to tell all the nesting species in the vicinity of the approach of any enemy. On two occasions at the Allegany School of Natural History there was a general alarm of all nesting species in a thicket close to my cabin. Catbirds, towhees, yellowthroats, song sparrows, and chestnut-sided warblers were all protesting with their characteristic calls, and robins and a red-eyed vireo came from the surrounding trees to see and join in. I investigated, and finally, in each case, saw a weasel wending its way through the blackberry vines.

Cleaning the nest consists of removing the excreta of the young. This is usually done after feeding. Sometimes the birds carry the excreta away, or they leave them on a branch or twig of a tree, and sometimes they swallow them. This differs in different species or at different stages in the growth of the young. In some species older young assist in this matter by voiding the excreta over the rim of the nest. With the dipper, which nests beside a mountain stream, the young back part way out of the nest opening and void their excreta into the brook below.

In addition to studying the behavior of parents and young in the nest, the development and growth of the young are important subjects, concerning which we need more information. The rate of growth is best determined by weighing the young birds each day, carrying into the field small scales capable of weighing in milligrams. A method of marking the young is necessary so that the gain in weight of each individual can be known accurately. This has been done in a few species only. Other measurements might be made, but that of weight is the most practical. Length measurements of a living young bird would be difficult to make with accuracy in the field.

Other studies of the development of altricial young should obtain information on the opening of eyes, the age at which first sounds are produced, and the acquirement of the juvenile plumage. For the latter one should be acquainted with the feather tracts and begin with a description of the newly hatched birds and the location of natal down by feather tracts. The time when sheathed feathers come through on each tract, and the time at which the sheaths begin to break should all be noted carefully. Very little is known definitely on this subject. Observers whose work on other points has been accurate and careful have been satisfied with hazy, indefinite descriptions of young in their early stages.

In explaining this sort of study to others I find a common, widespread belief that the touching or handling of eggs or young birds in the nest will cause the parents to desert them. Having handled eggs and young birds in the nest many times, and for a good many years, I can state that this has no basis in fact. Parent birds go on completing the nesting cycle though eggs are picked up, weighed, pencil-marked with numbers, and though the young are held in the hand, examined minutely, and sketched. It is true that birds sometimes desert nests that contain only eggs, but I have never known them to desert young, and when eggs are deserted it is just as likely to be when the eggs have never been handled. There is often a definite reason for the desertion, more serious than that someone handled the eggs. I believe that there is a higher percentage of desertion of late summer broods, which would indicate that desertion is caused by a waning of the nesting instincts as the time of postnuptial molt approaches.

On the other hand, there is such a thing as bringing danger to a nest by our actions around it. It is always well to approach a nest as quietly and unobtrusively as possible, and to avoid tramping down vegetation and disturbing the natural surroundings. Trimming away branches and leaves to make observation easier, or to permit photography, may expose the nest to rain, or too much sun, or to the view of natural enemies. In photographing I have often found that a branch that is in the way may be bent back temporarily, but in such a case it should be put back in the proper position before leaving the nest. Such things, in my experience, do not cause desertion of the nest, but they sometimes do cause a tragedy. A large percentage of nests is destroyed by natural enemies, the eggs or young, and even at times the parent birds, becoming victims. When such things happen, we cannot be sure whether it was our actions that brought it about or whether it would have happened anyway. The student of nests should expect such things to happen. One year when I had about forty nests under observation, only six of them succeeded in raising the young. One of the troubles that year was a torrential rain that flooded out a number of ground nests in a wooded swamp.

In a surprisingly short time after the young are hatched they are ready to leave the nest. The length of time varies from eight or ten days to two weeks or more. With larger birds, such as hawks, the time may be a month or more. With herons the young leave the nest as soon as they can climb around among the branches of the trees, and long before they can fly. They usually sit in a row on a branch, where the parent feeds them. The nest would be altogether too small to hold even one of them until full grown.

The appearance of altricial birds changes greatly in the short time they are in the nest. When ready to leave they are well covered with feathers, their eyes are fully open and bright, their tail feathers are still short, but the wing feathers have unsheathed to such an extent that they can fly. Some ground or low-bush nesters evidently leave the nest voluntarily a short time before they can fly, but I believe that birds that nest some distance above the ground do not leave of their own accord until they can.

Much has been said about parent birds teaching the young to fly, but the point is that young birds fly instinctively when their wing feathers are fully unsheathed. Until these wing feathers are developed, however, the young bird cannot fly, and no amount of teaching would make it do so. I once watched a young hummingbird leave the nest. It flew immediately, straight up, and perched in the top of the tree that contained the nest, and its parent was nowhere in sight when this happened. Parent birds may encourage young to leave the nest, and one way seems to be by ceasing to bring them food, thus encouraging them to go to the parent for food.

The first flight of a young bird is often clumsy and it usually finds difficulty in perching. But I have seen a young bluebird, in its first flight from the nest hole, go over a hundred and fifty yards and then perch high in a tree. I have seen young phoebes leave their nest under a bridge and fly out and up and perch without difficulty. But these are normal first flights when the bird waits until it is ready and leaves voluntarily. When young are frightened from the nest prematurely, it is often a different matter.

When young are still undeveloped and helpless in the nest, they show no fear. When a man approaches, they often respond by lifting the head and opening the mouth for food as they would at the approach of the parent. But when the time for leaving the nest is approaching, there is a considerable change. The young seem to acquire a sense of fear, to realize that the approaching man is not the parent. Then, if one approaches too closely, touches the nest or the branch to which it is fastened, they all leave at once, with an abruptness that is little less than an explosion. Under such conditions one or more individuals are likely to be unable to fly, but drop to the ground and scramble into the bushes and vegetation to the accompaniment of the frantic alarm notes of the parents. Under such circumstances the inexperienced bird lover will frequently catch the young and attempt to return them to the nest. But only rarely will they remain there, and it merely results in another tumble to the ground and scamper for concealment. One can sometimes put such a young bird on a perch where it is somewhat safer from natural enemies, but even that is difficult to accomplish.

The student of nesting will, after one or two experiences such as this, be careful about the nests he studies, not to approach too closely at such a time, so that the birds will leave naturally. None too many observations of the natural nest leaving have been made and reported, and it probably varies in different species and is well worth seeing and recording.

When young have left the nest, they are still in need of parental care for some time. Parents must feed them until they learn to find their own food. Just how long this is, is a matter we still know little about. It is difficult to keep track of a family of young birds after they have left the nest. Ordinarily, when we see parents with young birds out of the nest, we do not know how long the young have been out, nor how much longer they will need parental care. Very often the male cares for these young more frequently and for a longer time than the female. Perhaps, in some cases, the female is preparing for another nesting, but this would not apply to the last brood in summer, when care by the male is just as true as at other times.

I have known a pair of catbirds, whose second nest of the year contained only one young bird and three infertile eggs, to start construction of the third nest before the young bird left the second. The first egg of the third nest was laid three days after the young bird left. With only one bird to care for, the parents evidently had time to do this. It would be surprising if they did such a thing with a full brood. In fact, this happening seems to go beyond pure instinct and to suggest a bit of reasoning.

In another case a pair of bluebirds that had raised a brood in a bird box returned to the box after nine days with the brood of young with them. The young were still begging the male for food, for the female gave them no attention and was busy nest building. The young were observed to pick up earthworms without help, so they were evidently able to get their own food at that time.

Young are often reluctant to give up parental care and follow a parent about, begging for food and sometimes getting it, but often the parent captures an insect and swallows it in sight of the begging young, seeming to attempt to show them by example how to get their own food.

Not infrequently one may find a young bird, evidently a few days out of the nest, sitting on a branch and calling lustily for food, with no appearance of a parent for some time. Broods probably scatter somewhat, and this calling is evidently an aid to parents in finding lost young. The calls of young under such circumstances are different from other calls of the species. The sound is one evidently only used on such occasions, but recognizable to the parents. Until one knows these calls, they are unrecognizable. I have found quite a number of such birds by following up a sound I did not know, but there are still many species whose hunger calls are not familiar to me. Among the warblers there is a great similarity in these calls in different species, especially in the genus *Dendroica*. Most of these calls have never been described in ornithological literature.

I have mentioned the sense of fear acquired by young birds when about to leave the nest. This may not be possessed by all species. I am inclined to think that it is absent in some tree nesters, or at least in vireos. On a number of occasions I have found young red-eyed or blue-headed vireos sitting quietly on a low branch and showing no fear at my approach. In some cases the bird was approached, handled, and photographed by a number of different people, but showed no fear, and sat quietly wherever it was placed. The parents, in such cases, are temporarily absent. Possibly if they were around to give the alarm call, the case would be different, but that was not the case with one blue-headed vireo that came and fed the young bird with a number of people standing nearby.

SECOND NESTING

When young birds are at last able to find their own food, the nesting cycle is over. So far as we know, parents pay no attention to the young thereafter. Whether they recognize each other as young and parent in some future meeting is a matter we know nothing about. With most of the smaller songbirds, when the cycle is completed for the first time of the season, the parent birds start another nesting almost immediately, going back to the nest-building step and sometimes back to courtship. Occasionally they change mates at such a time, and there may be readjustments of territory, but I believe in the majority of cases the same pair of birds nest a second time in the same general locality. There is great variation in different species in the matter of second nestings, and many of the larger species have no normal second nesting. But with the smaller birds the majority have at least two nestings, and there may be three, or even four. Species that begin nesting activities in April and do not molt till late August may have time for four complete nestings, but much depends on the particular season. In some springs nesting starts late, and in some summers the season closes and molting begins earlier than usual. Much here depends on northern and southern localities, and a fourth brood may be more common southward. There seems to be some reason to believe that northward or in higher altitudes, where the season is shorter and the number of nestings fewer, the number of eggs in the nest averages a little higher.

When the nesting is broken up by some natural enemy or unfavorable weather conditions, the birds return to the beginning of the cycle, except in cases where this happens late in the season. When one of the mates is killed, the remaining bird seeks another mate. There are reports that, in such cases, the new mate may help finish the cycle with the eggs or young of the former parent. I believe that where a female with eggs is killed, the male will usually desert the eggs and start another nesting with a new mate, but a female that has lost her mate will finish the cycle alone. One case is reported where a male barn swallow attempted to kill the young of a female who had lost her mate. Cases are known where a male bird will continue care of the young alone when the female is killed.

There are often, and perhaps always, a certain number of unmated birds, and perhaps some that go through the whole season without a mate. A lone male, singing continually in a certain spot, day after day, is not certainly mateless because its mate is not seen. Certain species, especially tree nesters in forest areas, sing constantly through the period of incubation and seldom visit the nest, where the mate is incubating quietly. In such cases, unless the nest is found, the singing male could easily be thought to be a mateless bird, at least until the young hatch, when he assumes some activity about the nest. I doubt if the number of mateless birds is as great as some suppose it to be.

Finding and Studying Birds' Nests

THE knack of finding birds' nests seems to be one that a few people possess at the beginning, others acquire, but many never attain. A few kinds of nests, such as those of the osprey, are conspicuous and need no finding. But the majority of nests are more or less concealed and search is required to find them. One who would study nests must first find them or have someone else find them for him.

The season for finding nests is, with a few exceptions, from the middle of April to the middle of August, with the height of the season in June. This is true for northern United States, but farther south the season will begin earlier. The simplest way to find nests is to search through bushes and trees where birds are known to be. A great majority of species nest in bushes and trees and not far from the ground. A nest in a thick bush is not always easily seen. The bird is likely to put it where the bush is thickest and where leaves conceal it. This is particularly true if we try to look into the bush from outside. If one can contrive to get within a circle of bushes and get down on his hands and knees and look out from within, nests are more easily visible. This brings us to the point that nest hunting in real earnest is quite different from simply observing birds. We can do much of the latter from a road or a path, or even from the interior of an automobile. But when we hunt nests, we must leave the path and push through thick undergrowth or tall grass. We will get into thorns and briers and wade in swamps and marshes, climb trees, get down on our knees, or even lie on the ground and crawl. We become indifferent to scratches, mosquito bites, and wet feet. We should naturally be equipped for such things, with clothing that is strong and serviceable and that we expect will get both wet and dirty.

Ground nests, concealed in grass and weeds, or at the bases of thick bushes, are more difficult to find. We are not likely to find them by simply hunting. A great many are to be found by flushing the bird as we walk through grass or weedy places. Ground-nesting birds sit closely until we are almost upon them, and then flush almost under our feet. We must be alert to see such birds and try to make out just the point from which they come. Ground nests are carefully concealed, and if we are not sure within a foot or two of the point from which the bird flushed, we may search for a long time in vain.

In a number of species, such as the bobolink, which nest in the thick grass of meadows, the sitting bird is likely to leave the nest some time before the nest hunter approaches it. She runs under the grass and flushes from a point some distance away from the nest, which is then almost impossible to find. Such nests can be found by two persons working together, using a long rope which is dragged between them across the grass. Under such circumstances the bird flushes directly from the nest when the rope passes over it.

Tree nests that are built after the leaves are out are often difficult to find. A few, like those of the Baltimore oriole, are conspicuous, but most are not, and since they are above the line of ordinary vision, it is tiring work to search for them. Many are probably invisible from any point on the ground. But the number of nests of smaller birds that are high above the ground is comparatively few.

There are other ways of finding nests than simply searching for them. So long as we are merely searching for nests, without regard to the species, we can simply look here, there, or anywhere that a nest is likely to be. But when we get better acquainted with the nesting habits of particular species, we know just about where to look for such nests. If we know the birds and their songs, we should expect to find the nest of a particular species in the vicinity where the male sings regularly. Thus, when a yellow warbler sings, we search particularly in the elderberry bushes; when we hear the blue-winged warbler, we hunt in the centers of clumps of goldenrod stalks or other similar weeds; we stamp on the bank along the edge of the brook where the Louisiana water thrush occurs, or hunt about the bases of stumps or roots of large trees when the bird is a black and white warbler. Some birds tell us right where the nest is. Woodpeckers and other hole nesters have young that are exceedingly noisy when they are being fed. Blue-gray gnatcatchers are quite noisy when building their nests. Juncos get excited after their young are hatched, if one nears the bank where the nest is concealed. Nests in holes in trees may be found by tapping on the tree or stump till the bird flies out, but some hole nesters will not fly out for any amount of tapping. Sometimes such tappings brings out a flying squirrel or a white-footed mouse instead of a bird.

Most birds are quiet when the nest contains eggs, until we actually find it. But when there are young they often become nervous and start chipping. But the most excited chipping, among ground and low-bush nesters, comes after the young have left the nest, and sometimes our long search, with parent birds chipping about us constantly, ends in discovery of a fledgling sitting quietly on a low bush, or aroused when we almost touch it, fluttering away to some new place of concealment.

The nest of Wilson's snipe is likely to be in the center of the circle in which the male flies when going through his evening flight performance. It is on the ground in a grassy marsh, not concealed, but hard to see because of the protective color of the eggs. When the male is performing after dark, the female answers his sounds with a long squeaky call while sitting on the nest. One may line up the direction of this call from two different points, with conspicuous trees or other objects on the horizon, and mark the spots with stakes. These lines triangulate the position of the nest, and one may return in daylight and walk right to it.

Some birds perform ruses that attempt to lead the hunter away from the nest. The short-eared owl circles about and then drops to the ground on the side of the intruder that is opposite from the direction in which the nest lies and feigns injury. When the killdeer makes a great racket or feigns injury, we can be sure the nest is in some other direction than that of the noise and display. When ovenbirds have young, one bird will seek to draw attention to itself in one direction while the other creeps unobtrusively to the nest.

Often when we suspect the presence of a nest, our best method is to sit still and let the bird show us where it is. If we see a female hummingbird in the nesting season sitting on a small twig or flying about among the branches of trees where there are no flowers to attract her, it is well to watch her. The nest is small and difficult to see among the branches, but when she deliberately sits on it in front of our eyes, the difficulty is solved. A hummingbird around flowers, however, may be a long way from her nest, and when she darts away, following her flight with our eyes is practically impossible. Hummingbirds show little fear of men or of revealing the nest location. It is merely the small size, often combined with height above the ground, that makes the difficulty.

A parent bird with a bill full of insects is a pretty good clue to a nest full of young. Species and individuals, however, differ greatly in the readiness with which they will go to the nest while we watch. Tree nesters will generally go to the nest much more readily than ground nesters. Most hermit thrushes are extremely wild and unwilling to go to the nest while we watch, but a few individuals are remarkably tame and feed the young unconcernedly with several watchers nearby. I have also seen a veery that showed similar unconcern, revealing the nest and young almost as soon as I saw her, and later feeding the young without hesitation with four people and two cameras close by.

When we have found the nest, we should make the best possible use of our discovery by determining all the facts we can about it. If our time is limited and we cannot study it constantly, but can visit it daily or at frequent intervals, notes on its condition from day to day will prove of value. If we have time to devote to a complete study of nests, a question may arise. Having found a few nests, is it better to study those or go on finding more? Perhaps we will get a better general knowledge of nesting habits of birds by finding more, but we certainly can add new facts to ornithological knowledge if we study thoroughly the ones we have found. Even when others have studied that kind of nest before, there are likely to be new facts we can learn. Even though it is the same kind of nest we have studied before, we are likely to find that we did not learn everything in the first study.

When we find a nest at the beginning of the cycle, the opportunity to obtain new facts is greater. If we find it when it is still being constructed, there is opportunity to find out things about nest building first, and then all the other parts of the nest cycle. There is, of course, the chance that some accident or some natural enemy will keep the nest from completing its cycle. But the chances of learning new facts is greatest when we know just when the nest started and can see all the details from its beginning. Since a majority of nests found and studied are not discovered till incubation is started, and often not until they contain young, we know more about the late steps in the nest cycle than the early ones.

In studying nests the best work is done by the use of a blind —that is, a structure that can be set up temporarily—in which the observer stays. Birds soon become accustomed to a blind, and so long as they see no movement, they do not realize that an observer is within. When photography is the main object, results come more quickly when a blind is used. When one wishes to be very close to a nest under observation, a blind is necessary. Blinds have some disadvantages. They are an extra weight and bulk to carry, which makes considerable difference if a nest is a long distance from a road and across wild, rough country. If one is also carrying a camera and tripod and possibly other apparatus, this extra weight is something to consider. It is not always easy to see in more than one direction from an ordinary blind, and there are times when this is quite a disadvantage. Some birds get accustomed to an observer sitting near the nest as quickly as they do to a blind.

But it is important that birds should behave in a perfectly natural manner while under observation and that they be observed from close range, that we may see little details, such as the character of the food fed to the young. This is generally best accomplished by a blind. If, however, a blind is very close to a nest, too close to use field glasses for observation, one would still see just as well with field glasses from a more distant point, where a blind would not be necessary. A blind may be any sort of concealment, from a small, ordinary tent to a thick mass of brush, an old stump, or, in a marsh, a thick mass of cattails cut off and stuck up in the mud around the observer. The umbrella blind, first used and described by Dr. Chapman, has long been a favorite. A recent writer has recommended chicken wire, which can be carried flat, bent into any shape, and stuck full of leafy branches, weeds, or other vegetation to suit the location. There should be room inside a blind for the observer to be reasonably comfortable and for a camera and tripod, if photography is desired. While it is desirable to have a blind of dull color that blends with natural surroundings, it is not altogether necessary. White tents have been used successfully. The bird becomes accustomed to any object that is still. A camera need not be concealed. It soon becomes part of the surroundings to the bird, which may even perch on it.

When a blind is not used, the matter of sitting still is important. Birds fear something in motion. We must learn to sit without changing position, turning the head only very slowly, if at all, and lifting the hands or bird glasses very slowly. If mosquitoes are around, we use a mosquito repellent or let them bite. This is particularly important when one first starts to study a nest. It may take a long patient wait before the birds finally go to the nest, but once they have gone, they do so the second time much more readily, and soon thereafter are behaving normally and paying no attention to the observer.

For study without a blind, it is well to be dressed in dull, inconspicuous clothing. Khaki is a good color for naturalists to wear. My students have sometimes noticed the difference. A young lady who wore a white middy blouse had much more trouble watching nests than others whose clothing was more somber.

But there frequently come many cases where blinds and even sitting still prove not to be necessary. I once found a junco nest with young and, having my camera, decided to try for some pictures. I set up the camera, intending to tie a string to the shutter and hide behind some nearby shrubbery, but before I had finished focusing, one of the juncos came to the nest and fed the young, so that I watched the feeding on the ground glass. All I had to do was to sit beside the camera, about two feet from the nest, and squeeze the bulb when the proper time arrived.

Photography, when making a nest study, is often desirable. Good photographs will illustrate an article or other publication that we may contemplate. The pictures will help to show others just what the birds did and what they looked like. Moving pictures, and those in color when light conditions permit it, are especially desirable. But pictures are by no means necessary. The aim is likely to become only one of getting pictures and not of studying the bird. Even when the pictures are subordinate to the main purpose, our desire to get them may lead to forgetting to take notes.

Studying Bird Behavior

THE behavior of wild birds under natural conditions is determined chiefly by the struggle for existence. We have all heard of this before, but probably only the field naturalist who has obtained an intimate knowledge of the lives of wild creatures realizes the full force of that struggle. In order that wild creatures may survive there are three main things they must do. They must find food in sufficient quantity to keep them well, strong, and active; they must cope with their natural enemies and other dangers; and they must reproduce. The latter is not necessary for the welfare of the individual, but it is necessary for that of the species. Therefore, the individuals' instincts in that matter are as strong as they are for obtaining food and keeping out of danger.

Practically all of the things we see birds do have some relation to one of these three things. We are not justified, however, in supposing that the bird realizes these things and behaves accordingly, but only that it follows its instincts. When a bird builds its first nest, for example, there is no reason to suppose that it understands what the nest is for and what is going to happen. One instinct follows another throughout the nesting cycle, till the brood of young are finally out in the world. How much the bird remembers and realizes in its subsequent nestings is hard to say.

If we accept the Lamarckian definition of instinct as an inherited habit, there are unquestionably certain habits that birds acquire in a lifetime, such as returning to the same place where it has found a supply of food, or accustoming itself to an observer about its nest. Undoubtedly a bird learns by experience, and habits acquired in this way, not being inherited, are not, according to the definition, instinctive. They therefore indicate a certain degree of intelligence in birds. But so many actions of birds that undoubtedly are instinctive have been interpreted as intelligence that we should be wary of making such interpretations.

Though the struggle for existence is the main factor that determines the behavior of wild birds, there are often actions that have nothing to do with it, at least directly. The song of a bird has a definite relation to reproduction, but when birds sing in the fall, as many do, we cannot interpret such song in that way. Of course we might say that the birds are practicing, that they may sing better the following spring. But it isn't at all likely that the bird is practicing in any conscious way. It is simply singing because it possesses an instinct to sing and does not differentiate particularly between spring and fall.

When we watch individual birds, we note certain things in

Ovenbird, a songbird that walks

their behavior that are common to the species to which they belong. We note other things that are peculiarities of the individual. Actions common to the species are undoubtedly inherited. Those of the individual may be acquired.

There is undoubtedly among many birds a spirit of play. At times, when hunger is satisfied, enemies are not near, and the reproductive season is over, groups of birds, or even single birds, may go through actions that certainly seem to be only play. I have watched black ducks chase each other back and forth on the water; yellowlegs in fall migration fighting with each other in a playful manner; great blue herons doing a sort of aerial dance in the evening of a late summer day; and a lone loon, swimming about, splashing water, swimming first on one side and then on the other, rushing suddenly through the water for several yards, then lying still, head and all on the water, everything performed as if the bird found great enjoyment in its aquatic skill. These are all examples of behavior that have no direct relation to the struggle for existence.

The behavior of various kinds of birds when feeding is extremely variable. First of all, the behavior depends on the character of the food and where that food is to be obtained. Probably almost everyone has seen a robin pulling earthworms on the lawn. How many have watched a wood thrush turning over the dead leaves on the forest floor? The bluebird sees a grasshopper or beetle from a distant perch and flies out and pounces down upon it. The fox sparrow and the towhee do much scratching among the debris of a thicket. Then there are the warblers and vireos that obtain their food among the leaves and twigs of trees and shrubs; the creeper searching the rough bark of the large trees; the woodpecker drilling into a dead limb for the grub that is there; and the numerous catchers of flying insects—swallows, swifts, flycatchers, waxwings—all experts, but each going about it in its own way. About water we can watch kingfishers, terns, herons, and the osprey, each getting aquatic prey in a manner more or less its own. Even though herons all feed in a similar manner, waiting patiently and quietly and then lunging for their prey, yet each species has somewhat different mannerisms and attitudes in its fishing.

The character of food often determines whether certain species are solitary or gregarious. The shrike could hardly hunt in company with other shrikes and have any success. But flocks of sparrows and finches feed together, especially in winter, there evidently being sufficient quantity of the seeds they eat for all to have some. When birds eat wild fruits, different species often gather together. We may find half a dozen different species in a mulberry, shadbush, or wild-cherry tree. In the time of fall migration we find them in the dogwoods or the heavily fruited clusters of pokeberries.

Birds that feed on the ground in the open are likely to occur in flocks, probably not entirely because of the character of the food, but because the flock is a better protection from enemies and the lone bird in greater danger. Such birds are the horned larks, snow buntings, longspurs, rosy finches, and various species of shore birds. I have noted one most interesting method of flock-feeding on the ground among rosy finches. At certain times on the Western prairies food is evidently abundant on the ground. The flock moves over the ground in a definite direc-

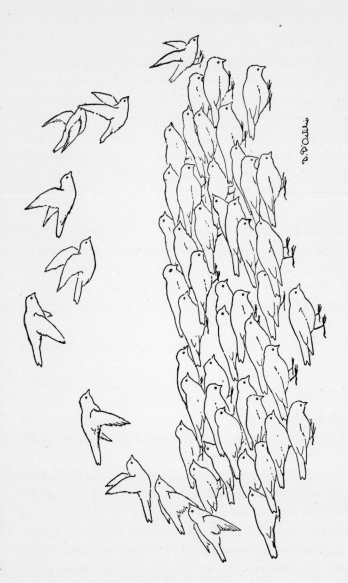

Rosy finches feeding on a prairie

tion, the birds keeping close together and every individual constantly moving and picking food from the ground as it goes. But for those birds at the rear of the flock, the ground is pretty well picked over and the food scarce. So, as each bird finds itself at the rear, it rises from the ground and flies over the flock to the front, where there is fresh picking. A constant stream of birds is continually flying over the flock as it progresses. This method is said to be used by snow buntings and perhaps by all the flocking, ground-feeding finches in open areas.

Altogether, the methods by which various birds obtain food are so varied and so interesting that, though much has been published about it, it seems well worthy of greater study. A book might be written on the subject by one who has had long field experience and taken copious notes. Such a study would require not only original observations, but a careful perusal of the literature, which is at present greatly scattered through many publications.

When feeding birds in winter, one may notice a great difference in the manner in which different species approach the food. When a piece of suet is fastened to the trunk of a tree and is eaten by several different species, one notes that the chickadees fly directly to it and cling to the bark as they eat; nuthatches fly to some place above it and come down the tree trunk head first; woodpeckers also alight above it, but they hitch down tail first, while the creeper flies to the bottom of the tree and creeps up.

When birds of the same species that glean food such as small insects or their eggs from twigs or foliage feed near each other, it is often noticeable that they call frequently. With food of such character, which is none too abundant, it is important that the birds do not feed too close together. It seems probable that these calls are for the purpose of keeping them apart. The late Dr. Joseph Grinnell first called attention to this matter and termed these sounds "sequestration notes." Little has been written about such notes, however, and there is a field here for more study. I believe that in the same manner the calls of owls that become common in late summer, after the young have left the nests, are sequestration notes. The calls are louder and carry a greater distance because the hunting territory of owls must necessarily be larger.

Birds use numerous ways to escape enemies. There are, among others, alarm notes; the habit of flocking, particularly for birds that live in the open; the use of cover for birds that live amid vegetation; the habit of "freezing"—that is, remaining perfectly still for a time—which is accompanied by protective coloration; and in protecting nest or young, the habit of feigning injury. The latter has been discussed earlier.

Most species of birds have some short, sharp call that serves as an alarm note. It is used whenever possible danger threatens. It is commonly used when an enemy is seen, and particularly when the nest or young are in danger. In many cases it serves to cause young to hide or freeze. In others it notifies all birds in the vicinity of the approach of an enemy. Birds, having wings, are not particularly concerned by an enemy on the ground, as far as they themselves are concerned, but when that enemy threatens nests or young they are much alarmed. They will follow a weasel or a cat through a thicket, keeping up a continual noise so that all may know just where the enemy is. Crows and jays are great alarmists, telling the entire woodland that an enemy is approaching. I have sometimes suspected that the calling of a flock of chickadees is of a similar nature.

When a winged enemy such as a Cooper's or sharp-shinned hawk appears, it is a different matter. Birds then take to cover and remain silent. There seems to be some sort of alarm at such times that tells the birds of the danger, for about a winter feeding station they all quiet down or freeze or disappear a minute or two before the hawk is seen, by human eyes at least. In fact, I have come to consider the sudden quieting of birds anywhere, at any time, as almost certainly foretelling the approach of a bird-killing hawk. On one such occasion a Cooper's hawk appeared in pursuit of a starling, and the pursuit continued on out of sight, so that I never knew its outcome. On another occasion, shortly after the quieting of birds, a ruffed grouse appeared, dropped to the ground about twenty feet from me, and scurried quickly under a dense green brier. Directly behind it was a goshawk, which, having missed its prey, sailed on into the distance.

Birds that live in the open, where there is no cover, commonly keep together in flocks. They feed together on the ground or shore line, rise and fly together, wheel about, and settle again, as if there were some definite leader; yet it is not apparent that there is such. Flocking is evidently a protection against enemies. Carnivorous animals that live on the ground would find difficulty in approaching a flock within striking distance, and even winged enemies evidently find it difficult to secure prey from a flock.

Once I stood on a reef during the fall shore migration. A flock of sanderlings was feeding about a hundred yards from me. Suddenly I noticed a larger bird flying toward the reef, low over the water. It proved to be a duck hawk. It was not flying toward the flock of sanderlings, but toward a point between the sanderlings and me. I then made out a single, lone sanderling that had strayed from the flock. It suddenly saw the duck hawk and rose and flew, but was hardly started in the air when the falcon seized it. The lone bird that strayed from the flock was the one in danger and the one that lost its life because its instinct to stay with the flock was not sufficiently strong.

In another year, at the same place and season, I was watching shore birds and terns as the tide was coming in. Suddenly a pigeon hawk in immature plumage appeared and dashed at a flock of semipalmated sandpipers. The sandpipers rose and wheeled about and the hawk made several attempts to capture one but missed each time. Possibly an older, more experienced bird would have singled out one sandpiper and succeeded in catching it. This occurrence, when compared with that of a previous year, taught me why such birds flock together.

In contrast to this, I once saw a northern shrike pounce upon a flock of tree sparrows feeding on the ground, single out one bird, and capture it. But the tree sparrow is a bird of bushes and weeds, depending more on cover than on the flocking habit, and the place was a feeding station, with grain scattered on the ground and no cover nearby. The shrike did not attack from the air, but dropped down from a tree and pinned its prey to the ground.

Kingbird in pursuit of a crow

For birds that do not naturally live in the open, the importance of cover is great. Bushes, tangles of vines, tall weeds, briers, and thick evergreens all make excellent cover. Such birds cannot live and compete with enemies without such cover. Yet man goes on clearing out bushes and weeds and tall tangles and often does just that in the name of conservation. I am reminded of an area where a few years ago there was a dense woods with an undergrowth of greenbrier and thick bushes. I visited it frequently, for there were many birds there. Today it is part of someone's country estate. The greenbrier, thick bushes, and smaller trees have all been thinned out. One can see through the woods in every direction, and among other things there are numerous nice, new, white-painted birdhouses fastened to the trees: testimony that the owner wanted birds on his place but didn't know how to encourage them. The problem of conserving bird life is not one of destroying predators but of supplying cover.

The habit of "freezing," or remaining perfectly still for a time when danger threatens, is practiced by many birds. It is particularly common with birds that live on or near the ground or young birds that have recently left the nest. Birds that practice it are usually protectively colored. In fact, protective coloration is only such when the animal so colored stays still. A good many protectively colored animals, birds, and insects have also directive marks that are conspicuous when they are in motion but not visible when they come to rest. Living creatures in the wild all seem to recognize the principle: Stay still and you are taken for part of the vegetation; move and you are conspicuous. The observer of the wild will do well to practice it also. Learn to freeze as the wild things do. Become part of the landscape, and wild creatures will behave naturally and come near and give you opportunities to see and know them better.

About winter feeding stations one may often observe freezing taking place all at once, and by all the birds in sight. When whatever is the mysterious signal comes that tells them there is danger, they all stop moving at once, wherever and in whatever position they may be. Once when two brown creepers were fighting with each other over the suet basket they suddenly froze. One was at the suet basket, its head slightly lifted as it was about to feed. The other was an inch or two to one side, with one of its wings slightly spread. I glanced at the clock and timed them. They held those positions without a visible movement for fourteen minutes. Then the bird at the suet slowly lowered its head, and the other one closed its wing and darted at the first one to drive it off. Another mysterious signal had told them that the danger was over. Watching things like this from within a house has one disadvantage: we cannot see the cause of the trouble. Perhaps, had I been outside, the "cause" would have seen me and kept away and there would have been no freezing. I have usually seen my best examples of freezing at a winter feeding station from within.

Feathers, Plumages, and Colors

THE detailed study of plumages belong to the indoor student of birds rather than to the outdoor. But there are things about feathers and plumages that the outdoor man should know so that he may better understand the lives of the birds he studies. There are also some phases in the study of plumages and markings that ought to be strictly the outdoor man's province. There has been much theorizing about colors and markings and their significance, some of it not based upon actual observation of the live bird and not considering the real environment in which it lives. The outdoor man can help to throw much light on the true significance of colors and markings if he understands what the problems are.

Feathers are structures peculiar to birds. No other living creature has true feathers. In fact, a good definition of a bird is "any animal that has feathers." A number of birds are known that have no wings, and many more that, though they possess wings, cannot fly. But no kind of bird is known that does not have feathers.

There are a number of different kinds of feathers, but the ones that chiefly concern the field student are of three sorts. The small feathers that cover the body of a bird are called contour feathers. The larger, stiff feathers that make up the tail and the outer half and tips of the wings are flight feathers. The third kind of feather is the down that occurs on most newly hatched young and beneath the contour feathers of many birds, particularly water birds.

When birds whose young are altricial are newly hatched, their bodies usually have some down on them. When the young are precocial, they are quite heavily covered with down. The down is attached to the tips of the feathers that are beneath the skin and grow out later. When these contour or flight feathers grow out, they are closely wrapped in sheaths and look more like quills than feathers. Anyone who has picked a chicken has seen these so-called pinfeathers. They may be observed readily in young songbirds in the nest when these young are four or five days old. Soon after these feathers grow out, the sheaths begin to break at the tips, and the vane of the feather begins to show. The breaking of the sheath continues until the feather is fully out and the sheath drops off. This happens at different times in different parts of the body, so that the bird is not fully feathered until the last feathers are unsheathed. In a few birds, such as the cuckoos, the feathers remain sheathed until the bird is about ready to leave the nest, and then the sheaths all break at once, in a very short time. Just before the sheaths break, the bird's appearance is suggestive of a small porcupine.

In many birds, including the common songbirds, the feathers do not grow out all over the body, but in special places, called feather tracts. When feathers are unsheathed, they spread out and cover the body, so that the tracts are not apparent, but on a young bird in the nest the tracts may be seen easily. The natal down of the newly hatched bird occurs on some of these tracts, but in passerine birds, at least, not on all of them. Which tracts have the feathers preceded by down varies in different families, genera, and species. One may make observations on this matter when examining newly hatched young in the nest. The down which the young bird has when newly hatched is called the natal plumage. Accurate descriptions of natal plumages in the literature of ornithology are very few. The matter probably has taxonomic value, but few collections of birds in the natal plumage have been made and still fewer of them studied. In fact, a complete description of the new-hatched passerine birds can best be made from living birds in the nest. In preserved specimens, colors are likely to change. The outdoor student can add greatly to our knowledge if he studies and describes these newly hatched young.

Points to cover in the descriptions are color of the skin; color of the swollen portions at the base of the bill; color of the mouth lining; and color and distribution of the down in feather tracts. The skin is usually flesh-colored, but it varies in different species in its tendency to shade from grayish toward yellowish or somewhat orange shades in some, toward rosy pink or brick color in others, and a dark gray that is almost black in a young catbird. The swollen part of the bill is generally yellow, but it may be rich yellow or pale cream color or, according to my observations, white in the vesper sparrow. The inside of the mouth may be yellow or pinkish-flesh color or deep pink. The pinkish colors are common to finches and warblers, while in most other families the color is yellow. Recorded observations on the matter are few and fragmentary and need verification in many species.

The natal down varies from white to dark gray or brown in different passerine species. It is long in the phoebe, so that, though it grows out only in particular places, it nearly covers the entire upper parts. It is very short in the barn swallow, hardly serving as a cover at all. A few species, such as the magpie, blue jay, cedar waxwing, English sparrow, and yellow-breasted chat have no down at all. Other species have down only on the head and back. In other species it occurs also on parts of the wings or on the lower sides. A few species have a small tuft of down on the tail, and others just above the heel joint on the legs. The phoebe also has down on its eyelids. Almost all of these statements are from my own previously unpublished observations. For many more such facts, observations have apparently never been made.

The development and growth of the contour and flight feathers after the down stage are subjects concerning which details of different species are not too well known. Careful notes when observing a nest, stating the age of young when the first feathers of each tract come through, when these feathers begin breaking the sheaths, and when they are entirely unsheathed, are highly desirable, such information being at present available for only a few species.

The feathers that grow out following the down constitute

the juvenal plumage, and the falling of the down is, in a sense, the first molt of the young bird and has been called the post-natal molt. In a large majority of species, the juvenal plumage is somewhat different from the plumages of adult birds. The student should acquaint himself with the characters of the juvenal plumage of each species, as far as he is able, and consider that his knowledge of the colors and markings of each species is not complete till he can identify birds in juvenal plumage as readily as he does adult birds. In fact, he should rejoice at the opportunity to study and know the juvenal plumage of a bird just as much as he does when he sees a species new to him. Too many field students stop their knowledge of a species when they have seen an adult male. Though the plumages of females and young are less brilliant, they are not less interesting or less worthy of study.

In a majority of cases, where sexes differ in plumage, the young bird has a plumage that resembles that of the adult female. But there are other cases where the plumage is different from either adult. In considering these juvenal plumages, one should have an understanding of the theory of recapitulation. This is the theory that young organisms go through stages or conditions that resemble those of the ancestors of the species. Thus the speckled breasts of young robins and bluebirds are believed to indicate that ancestors of the thrush family had speckled breasts. Juvenal plumages of all members of this family are not only speckled on the breast, but streaked with light color on the upper parts. One will find many cases where this theory seems to apply, both to plumages and other characters. But there are numbers of other cases where it does not apply at all. Consequently the idea remains theoretical, and we cannot work out all the changes that ancestors went through by observing the development of the young. Any observations that may bear upon this theory as a whole are worthy of record, for not only physical characters, but habits and instincts, best observed in the field, may indicate recapitulation or the lack of it.

Juvenal plumages may be seen at any time after the first young leave the nest until the late summer, when the young undergo the postjuvenal molt. In most species the time of this molt is August, but it varies from June to September, and in flycatchers and swallows takes place even later, after they have migrated. With some of the warblers the postjuvenal molt takes place soon after the young have left the nest. In fact, they may be molting some of the feathers at the time they leave, and are sometimes still being fed by the parent after they have molted into the first winter plumage.

One should be careful to distinguish between juvenal and immature plumages. The first winter plumage, after the post-juvenal molt, if different from that of the adult, is an immature plumage. This may be unlike both the juvenal plumage and that of the adult. Plumages of young birds seen in late summer may be juvenal or immature, according to the species. Thus the gray-colored tree swallows of late summer are birds in juvenal plumage, whereas the yellowish-green and white chestnut-sided warblers seen in August are in the first winter, or immature, plumage. With species that have several broods of young in a year the postjuvenal molt may come at different times, the young of the first brood molting much earlier than

Adult black tern drops food to a juvenile bird

those of the last. Usually the postjuvenal molt is partial; that is, not all of the juvenal feathers are shed. Usually the wing feathers, or some of them, are retained to form part of the first winter plumage.

All birds molt their feathers at least once a year, and often twice. After the postjuvenal molt, each bird has one complete molt each year, after the breeding season, known as the postnuptial molt. This usually comes in late summer or fall. In late winter or early spring there may be another molt, known as the prenuptial. This molt is entirely absent in some species; very slight in others that shed just a few feathers of the head or about the base of the bill; covering a large part of the body feathers but not the wings and tail in others; and entirely complete in a few.

In some species the feathers worn between postnuptial and prenuptial molts are quite different from those worn between prenuptial and postnuptial, causing the difference between winter and summer plumages. The male scarlet tanager is a well-known example of this, in which the change of the body feathers from bright red to dull green and yellow and then back to red again is spectacular. The wing and tail feathers, in this case, are shed but once a year, and after the bird is fully adult are always entirely black. In the first year of life, however, the young male has brownish feathers in the wings which distinguish it from the completely mature male. One may find male tanagers in late summer going through the postnuptial molt and patched with green, red, yellow, and black. If one chances to see male tanagers in September, just before they leave for the South, he will see them in full winter plumage.

Careful examination of male tanagers, when they first arrive in spring, will reveal birds that have not quite completed the prenuptial molt, but the full prenuptial molt cannot be observed in the summer range of this tanager. Those who live farther south may see similar molts in the summer tanager.

Similarly one may see numerous other peculiarities in plumage conditions if he keeps constantly on the watch at all seasons. It is not at all difficult to see goldfinches in various stages of prenuptial molt in early spring. A year-old male redstart in the midst of its first postnuptial molt and a male towhee or cowbird in the postjuvenal are interesting sights. Such birds often puzzle the observer who is not acquainted with molts, and sometimes lead him to think he has found a new bird not described in the books.

The molts of ducks are peculiarly different from those of other birds. The postnuptial molt begins in late spring or early summer, and the drakes, which in most species have a much brighter and gaudier plumage than the females, become dull in color and rather like their mates, a condition known as the "eclipse" plumage. The molt continues most of the summer, the flight feathers usually being shed after the body feathers. In late summer or fall comes the prenuptial molt, and then the drake returns to its bright plumage, which is worn through the winter. The bright winter plumage is the breeding plumage, for most ducks court and choose mates in late winter or early spring, often long before nesting begins.

After being worn for some time, feathers show some wear at their tips or around the edges. Light-colored feathers, especially white or pale brown or buff shades, wear more rapidly than black or richer colors. Because of this, birds undergo considerable change in appearance owing to wear of the feathers between molts. In many cases the bright colors or blacks of birds are veiled by duller tips just after the molt. These tips gradually wear off, and the colors and markings brighten or become more definite. In other words, worn plumages are often brighter in appearance than fresh ones. This led to the erroneous conclusion that feathers actually changed in color, and one may sometimes find statements to that effect in the literature of fifty years ago or more.

The changes caused by wear alone are sometimes remarkable. In early fall the male English sparrow appears to have lost his black bib. Next spring the bib is there, clear and sharply defined, though he has not molted since the previous summer. But the bib was there all the time, hidden beneath the grayish feather tips that veiled it. The starling changes from the heavily speckled plumage of fall to the iridescent black of the following summer by merely wearing off the speckles. The shape of feathers makes some difference in birds' markings. In the starling, the feathers taper to long lanceolate tips, so that the buff color at each tip forms speckles. But on the breast of the robin the feathers have broad, rounded tips, and the white-edged feathers in fall give the appearance of fine white scalloped marking against the red of the breast. But these scallops are practically all worn off by the following spring. In the spring the "livelier iris" and "brighter crimson" of Tennyson's well-known poem come not by molt nor change in color, but entirely by wear.

The changes that take place in the bobolink and the snow

bunting owing to wear of the feathers are quite remarkable. These have been studied, described, and figured. The student should familiarize himself with them and all other plumage changes that take place in his region. He should seek to see and know as many as possible of these.

Much has been said and written about the colors and markings of birds and the relations of these to their lives. Numerous theories have been advanced as to how these markings serve the bird as adaptations. Some of these theories seem to have been propounded by those who know little of the live bird in its natural environment. To be of any real value, they should be checked by field observation, making another opportunity for the outdoor student.

The colors and markings of birds are believed to be of three main sorts: protective, attractive, and directive. There are a few others besides these that have been suggested, but the majority of markings are supposedly these three.

That many birds are protectively colored under the right sort of field conditions cannot be denied. That the markings vary according to the environments in which they live is quite obvious. Birds that live in grassy areas in the open are inclined to be striped on the upper parts, like the meadowlark and the female bobolink. Those that live in the shade of forests are inclined to plain colors on the back, like the thrushes. Those with uncovered nests on the ground, in thickets, or wooded areas are likely to be mottled in various light and dark shades, like the woodcock and the whip-poor-will. Birds that live in the foliage of trees are either dull greenish, like the vireos and the female tanagers, or marked in patches of various colors, like the warblers. In many cases we can correlate colorings with environment. But when we try to apply the rule in every case, we find numerous exceptions.

Some years ago an artist-naturalist, Abbott Thayer, published a book, *Concealing Coloration in the Animal Kingdom.* In it he attempted to show that all kinds of colorings were protective or concealing. The book was sharply criticized, and while some of the criticisms were probably just, they perhaps led many to pay too little attention to some of the enlightening facts brought out by the author. One of these, the principle of "obliterative coloration," stated that a large number of animals are darker in color above and lighter below, and that in a strong light this darkened the lighted parts and lightened the shadows, causing the animal to become almost invisible against a background of its own color. At the same time it was shown clearly that an animal—or, for that matter, an inanimate object—was easily seen if it was just as dark below as above. If an object obliteratively colored was turned upside down, it was immediately conspicuous. But these experiments are ones controlled to bring about the result of obliteration. The questions of importance are, first, how often do wild creatures, under natural conditions, occur against a background of their own color and under conditions that bring about obliteration; and, second, how often does such coloring protect them from natural enemies? Observations in the field are needed to answer such questions.

Another of Mr. Thayer's points is that of camouflage. Certain animal forms, particularly well illustrated in the shore birds, are colored in patches, bands, and stripes of conspicuous colors. But when these markings are seen against a background of dark and light and patchy colors, the form of the animal is not clearly made out. Its outline is not clear and it does not look like an animal or anything alive. A turnstone standing on a pebbly beach is a good example. Anyone looking at a mounted turnstone or a colored picture of one will agree that it is a most conspicuous bird. But anyone who has tried to see one standing on a stony beach where the pebbles are dark and light, reddish and brown and white, with black shadows beneath them, will realize that the turnstone is anything but conspicuous so long as it stays still.

The factor that seems to me of greatest importance in this discussion of coloration or obliterative character is the question of motion or lack of it. When the animal is still, its coloring helps to hide it or obliterate it or make it seem part of the background. This may also be true, to a somewhat lesser degree, of a slowly moving animal. To find an animal that sits or stands still in natural surroundings is always difficult. Even when there is some slight motion, this is often the case. It is quite difficult, for example, to find a singing bird that perches in one spot and moves only slightly when singing. Though the song gives a clue to its position, it is still hard to see if the perch is low and against foliage.

But when any creature, bird, mammal, or insect moves rapidly, I cannot agree that there is anything concealing or obliterative about it. Mr. Thayer contends that the white marks on the tails, backs, and wings of animals, which are visible only when the animal is in motion, are obliterative; for the enemy, looking at them from a lower position than man, will see the white marks against the sky as part of the sky. But it seems to me that the enemy cannot help seeing that something is in motion and that that something is alive. Nor in forested areas would they be seen against the sky, even from a lower position. My contention is that, however concealingly or obliteratively colored an animal may be, when it is in motion such coloration has no effect. But the student, after having some experience in field work, should form his own opinion.

In wild animals of many kinds there are numerous examples of species that are extremely difficult to see when at rest but are instantly conspicuous as soon as they start to run or fly. On some portion of the anatomy that is hidden when at rest but shows conspicuously the moment rapid motion begins there are patches of white or bright colors. Consider the white-tailed deer, the cottontail rabbit, the meadowlark, flicker, yellowlegs, willet, turnstone, and, among insects, grasshoppers and the underwing moths. It is as though nature meant the moving animal to be instantly conspicuous and easily followed as long as it continues in motion, and at the same time extremely inconspicuous and hard to see the moment it comes to rest.

In fact, the more one sees of animal life in the wild, the more he becomes impressed with the importance of motion, or the lack of it, in relations between a predatory creature and its prey. This is particularly true with birds, for their eyesight is very keen. They evidently depend on it more than on hearing or smell, in detecting the presence of other creatures, whether the others are enemies or prey.

The white or bright-colored marks that show in a running or flying creature are examples of directive coloration. Whatever purpose they serve in the life of the creature, they certainly aid man in naming them. In each species of bird that has a directive mark, that mark is distinctive. With ducks, for example, marks in the wings usually name the species when it is in flight. However different the two sexes may be, these directive marks are possessed by both, and also by the young when they are able to fly. It seems logical to assume that these marks aid individuals in recognizing others of their species. Most birds that flock together have such marks, and they evidently aid in keeping flocks together and in warning individuals of the approach of an enemy when the keenest bird of the flock detects the enemy and starts to fly.

The more brilliant colors of birds, particularly those that are characteristic of the male bird, are examples of attractive coloration. One of the chief points about such coloration for the field student to observe is the matter of display of these colors. Birds often go through certain actions that show off these colors, and the cases where this is true are so numerous that it seems hardly doubtful that such colors are for display. But such display is by no means confined to the season of courtship and often takes place when no mate is present. It seems difficult to understand, in such cases, just how this habit of displaying serves the bird. It may be, however, that the display becomes a habit, just as does singing, and its performance at the wrong season is similar to singing in the fall.

Many have seen the redstart displaying by spreading its tail. That it also displays the breast marks by sitting up nearly straight and puffing them out is perhaps not so well known. The redwing's display with each song is commonly observed.

When this bird is not displaying or singing, but perching quietly, the red wing patch is hidden beneath the feathers of the sides. This is also true of other birds that have conspicuous colors on the wrist joint, which is commonly called "shoulder." Students often say, "I can't seem to see the bay-colored patch on the vesper sparrow's wing." It isn't often visible in field observation and is much less useful in identification than the marks on the side of the head. I have seen many colored pictures of blue-winged teal sitting in the water, with the bright blue patch showing conspicuously. But I do not remember ever seeing it in the field on a swimming bird. It shows plainly enough in flight, but a swimming bird shows only the green speculum mark.

That birds have characteristic habits of display that go with the special markings is well illustrated by the killdeer and the Wilson snipe. Each of these species has a conspicuous patch of orange-brown. It is on the lower back of the killdeer, but on the tail of the snipe. Both birds display by crouching, lowering the wings, and spreading the tail. But the killdeer lowers the tail and raises the back, whereas the snipe raises the tail till it is at about right angles to the back. Thus, by this difference in habit, each species displays its special mark.

Other kinds of coloration than the three mentioned are described by writers. A large bird of prey may be concealingly colored—a snowy owl on a snow-covered prairie, for example —but this is not protective coloration, for it conceals the bird not from its enemies, but from its prey. The bright-colored patch on the kingbird's head, which is usually concealed and seldom seen in the field, is supposed to be used to attract insects, the insect mistaking the bright color for a flower. Evidently this use of the color patch has not been observed frequently. If it is used in such a way, it needs verification by field observers.

In fact, all through the field of coloration we need observations to verify or disprove theories that have been advanced. One point worth keeping in mind is the similarity of patterns and colorings of unrelated species that have similar habits and habitats. Why, for example, do bobolinks, lark buntings, longspurs, and horned larks all have the under parts black or marked with black? All of them dwell in the grass and are flight singers. Such things as these may occur to the thoughtful observer and present problems that may be possible to solve. The significance of some birds' markings is fairly obvious, but there are many others that are not obvious at all.

The Study of Songs and Calls

THE bird lover values a knowledge of bird songs because it helps him to identify birds. The field ornithologist values it because it aids him in following the migration or in making a list or census of the birds in a particular area. But aside from these aims, there is reason for paying more careful attention to songs and to their details for the sake of the study of songs themselves. There are many things we wish to know about the songs of birds but few seriously scientific students in the field attempting to discover them.

Anyone who has learned to recognize the songs of different species in the field can add to our knowledge by keeping notes on the seasons of songs; the time of day when singing is most or least abundant; the succession of species in the morning awakening, or the ceasing of song in the evening; the number of songs per minute or hour under difficult conditions; the relations of singing frequency to weather, light intensity, or other factors; the relation of song to the nesting cycle, and many similar things. But the study of variations in song, which may be seasonal, geographical, or local, and the descriptions of songs require an especially good ear for song and a training in musical principles and the physics of sound.

People vary greatly in the ear they possess for musical sounds, in distinguishing differences in pitch, time, loudness, quality, and phonetics. One who cannot recognize tunes and sing or whistle them accurately, even though he can recognize bird songs, should not attempt descriptions of songs or study of variations, except perhaps through the indoor study of records made by a mechanical recording device. Such a study does not require use of the ear, but an analysis of the sound track on a film by microscopic observation.

But there are many people who possess good ears for music and know bird songs who might contribute to this study but do not do so because of lack of musical knowledge. Frequently such people think it is a lack of ear that is the handicap, when it is only a lack of knowing how to describe what the ear hears. They are in the same position as one who might try to describe bird plumages without knowing the names of colors. We have learned to name colors from early youth and, unless we are actually color blind, have no difficulties. But most of us have not learned to name pitches of sounds. When in the field I might remark that the interval between two notes in a bird song is a tone and a half or a minor third, someone is likely to remark, "You have an unusual ear for music." But it is not that my ear is better than a great majority of others, but that I know what to call the pitch interval I hear. Anyone who is not "pitch-deaf," if I may use such a term to correspond to color blind, may learn to know these things. He may learn to recognize an octave, a fifth, a tone, a half tone, or other interval. He may study the simple principles of the physics of sound, apply it to bird songs, and thus be equipped to describe songs accurately, to make records of them, and launch forth into the field of study of variations in bird song.

Among some bird lovers there seems to be a bit of confusion as to what is a bird song and what is not. Birds produce many sounds that are more or less musical, but not all of them are songs. A song, to be such, must fulfill two conditions. It must be chiefly or entirely a performance of the male, and it must be used mainly, or entirely, at a definite season of the year, the season of reproduction. It is difficult, however, to make a more absolute statement than this, for there are numerous cases of performances that are unquestionably songs yet do not fulfill one or the other of these conditions perfectly. In a number of species, the female sings more or less, but I know of no species in which the female sings as definitely, frequently, and certainly as the male. There is probably more female singing than we know, for it is impossible to distinguish sexes in the field in many species. But it still seems to be true that song, in every species, is mainly a masculine character.

There is also great variation in the extent to which song is confined to a definite season. Such species as the song sparrow and the meadowlark may be heard singing in every month of the year. But they are silent for a time, in the period of post-nuptial molt, and song is never so frequent and certain in fall or winter as it is in the season of mating and nesting. Consequently songs do fulfill these two conditions mainly, and in every species, even though there are occasional exceptions.

A song need not be musical to our ears, nor is every musical bird sound a song. The "conqueree" of the redwing is undoubtedly a song. It is strictly confined to the male and the season of nesting. It is given from a perch, or on the wing, in a singing manner, accompanied by display of the red wing patches, and it is pleasingly musical. The yellow-headed blackbird goes through very similar performances in every way, except that the final sound produced is not pleasingly musical, but a ludicrous squawk. Many would be unwilling to call such a sound a song, but from our definition it undoubtedly is.

Whenever a bird sings normally, its song is recognizable as to species. Anyone who knows the song of that species will be able to name the bird. Because of this, there seems to be an idea on the part of many bird students that the songs of all birds of a species are alike and that the description of one song is a description of the song of the species. This idea has unfortunately been fostered through the recording of songs by sound-reproducing devices, for in most cases a single song has been recorded and is announced as *the* song of *the* species, whereas it actually is *a* song of one individual of that species. Other individuals would sing the song somewhat differently, and that individual would probably have several more ways of singing. When a recorded song is fairly typical of the species, it is helpful in teaching students to know songs. But when that song is not very close to the more typical form, as is frequently the case, it is likely to confuse the student who attempts to hear the same song again from a living wild bird. Though most

Hooded warbler singing

songs have something about them that is characteristic of the species and are recognizable, there is great variation. It is often difficult to find two songs of the same species that are alike. The song of the Baltimore oriole, for example, is exceedingly variable. Birds in one locality may sing songs that are rather similar to each other, but in another locality, only a short distance away, the songs are quite different. Yet the basic notes of which they are composed, and the quality of these notes, are such that a song is practically always recognizable to the experienced bird student.

In most species not only do individuals differ from each other in their songs, but each individual has a number of songs, and these are somewhat varied, sometimes with the season and sometimes with the time of day. Each individual song sparrow has a whole repertoire of songs, and each one is likely to be different from the songs of other individuals. In the height of the nesting season, after the nest is established and incubation has begun, each male sings his songs with considerable regularity in the early morning. Each song is repeated a dozen times or so and then another taken up. Studying one individual for a number of mornings will generally reveal about the limits of its song variations. The number of different songs may vary from six to twenty or more, but the extreme of variation is a matter of interpretation of the observer. Just how much variation constitutes a different song? Some individuals are likely to make performance of a song slightly different by variations, particularly in the terminal notes. Yet when a really new song is sung, it is different throughout.

Many other species beside the song sparrow have varied

songs and a particular manner of singing. Each species is a study in itself, and comparatively little has been recorded about these manners of singing. One surprising thing is the likeness in form of song in totally unrelated birds. The habit of alternating two different songs is common to the towhee, redstart, and meadowlark, and probably other species. A long vocal performance, beginning with rapid notes and ending with retarded slurs or two-note phrases is found in such unrelated birds as the pied-billed grebe, Florida gallinule, laughing gull, and yellow-billed cuckoo, but I know of no passerine species that sings in this way. The habit of repeating a song two or three times in succession, without a pause, is common to the purple finch and the ruby-crowned kinglet. If we classified birds by the likenesses in their songs instead of their anatomy, our classifications would be totally different.

A good many of the variations in the singing of individual birds are seasonal, or vary with the conditions of the nesting cycle. Thus the meadowlark sings regularly for nearly two months before the season of mating begins, and it is during this period, in late March or early April, that it is likely to alternate two different songs. In late April, when courtship and mating begin, it sings one song after another, repeating each song a number of times and producing a much greater number of songs than the song sparrow. But unlike the song sparrow, these songs are not distinctly different from those of other meadowlarks. Certain of them are very common songs of the species, apparently sung by every meadowlark in the region and often repeated by first one bird and then another. After nesting is established, song becomes somewhat less abundant and variable but may be heard regularly till August, when the nesting is over and the postnuptial molt begins. Song is generally resumed in September and may be heard fairly regularly through the fall and even occasionally in winter months.

The commonest and best-known song of each species is the territory song, the song first used when the male has selected a territory and is singing to warn away other males and to advertise his need of a mate. To accomplish these purposes this song must be loud, frequently repeated, and distinctive of the species. Such songs, heard frequently in the spring and earlier part of the nesting season, become extremely familiar to bird students. Those students who search for birds mainly in the May migration are often unacquainted with the fact that some birds sing other and sometimes quite different songs later in the season.

A good many of the warblers have two distinctive types of songs, singing sometimes one and sometimes another. With some warblers, such as the black-throated green, these two types are both common, and there seems to be no rule of season, time of day, or individuality that determines which of the songs will be used. Apparently both can serve as a territory song. But with some of the other warblers there is a fairly definite seasonal difference in the two songs. It is well marked, for example, in the black and white, blue-winged, and chestnut-sided warblers. In the spring these birds arrive, singing the common territory song; the "weesy weesy" of the black and white, the two wheezy notes of the blue-winged, and the "pleased to meet you" song of the chestnut-sided. But as the season advances, evidently after nesting is established, a new song begins to be heard now and then. The black and white breaks its chain of "weesys" for some irregular, lower-pitched notes; the blue-winged sings an altogether different song of four or five varied notes rather than two; and the chestnut-sided has a special song, with some notes near the end still high and accented, but with no definite "meet you" at the end. These songs are less well known but not uncommon, and can be heard by any observer who keeps watch through the season in localities where these species breed. Such songs, coming when the birds are actually nesting, are probably best termed the nesting songs. Just what their significance is, is a matter to be worked out. It is noticeable that the common territory song is not entirely abandoned at this season, and with the blue-winged warbler the nesting song is used in late summer, after the postnuptial molt.

In the very brief period of courtship there are sometimes songs of peculiar character that are little known because they come so infrequently and last for so short a time. With a number of species, such songs are likely to be faint, of the type that have been called "whisper songs," and except for that, they are much like territory songs in form. In a few cases courtship songs are flight songs, though most flight songs seem to be something else that comes later in the season. With the meadowlark the courtship song is a flight song, coming in April, a peculiar performance of different and less musical character than the territory song. This is true in both eastern and western meadowlarks. The song is not common, however, and sometimes years go by without my hearing it.

Flight songs, whether they are courtship songs or not, are of

McCown's longspur in parachute flight song

considerable interest. Each species that sings in flight is worthy of special study, for the conditions are different in almost every one. Some birds sing only occasionally in flight, but it seems quite likely that almost every species may sooner or later be observed in flight song. Many of these, however, are apparently mere accidents. A bird in migration, and singing as it feeds in the treetops, now and then happens to sing as it flies from one point to another. But other species, particularly ground and low-bush nesters, vary the song and prolong it when in flight, rising in flight and singing in a sudden ecstatic outburst.

A few birds, such as Sprague's pipit, sing mainly, if not entirely, in flight. Bobolinks and longspurs sing more frequently in flight than from a perch. Birds like the ovenbird, yellow-throat, and mourning warbler have a special flight song, quite different from the more common territory song. Such songs are generally sung as the bird rises, ceasing when it reaches a certain height and drops back to the ground silently. The longspurs, however, rise silently and begin singing at the high point, floating downward to the grass as they sing. The ovenbird rises above the treetops and progresses a long distance as it sings, usually turning about and flying back at a lower level when the song is over. The Townsend solitaire may go through elaborate twisting and turning flights or hover in one spot for a long time, singing continually. The ludicrous clownlike flight song of the chat is still another variation.

One may observe some species for years without knowing that they sometimes have a flight song. Such has been my experience with several species: first with the seaside sparrow, and more recently with the Canada warbler. Yet there are some birds that apparently never sing in flight. I have never observed a flight song from any of the thrushes or the vireos. Why certain birds do not sing in flight is just as interesting a question as why others do.

With a good many species flight song is a phenomenon of late summer and evidently has no relation to the nesting. There is perhaps good reason to think that such songs are of more or less primitive nature. Their rambling, indefinite character would also indicate this. Therefore, flight song may be regarded as a phenomenon of past ages that today is gradually disappearing.

There is a tendency of some species of birds to elaborate their songs in late summer, at the time the nesting season is about to close and before the postnuptial molt has begun. Some species simply lengthen their songs, while others add notes of a somewhat different character. Some, like the field sparrow, may sing their regular song over and over without pause. These kinds of songs need study, for very little has been noted about them, and there are only vague surmises as to why such songs exist.

In late summer, early fall, and occasionally early spring, one may hear faint warbling songs that are rambling, indefinite, and often prolonged. They may be twitters, warbles, or trills, or all three mixed. Such songs are usually inaudible from any great distance. When we succeed in identifying the singer, we may find it to be a wren, sparrow, catbird, or almost any species. These songs have been referred to in literature as "whisper songs," but the term that gives a better idea of the meaning is "primitive songs." The theory is that once the an-

A singing chickadee

cestors of singing birds sang a song like this, before the development of more definite territory songs took place. Today birds return to these songs at seasons when regular singing is ceasing or just beginning. Evidently young birds that have never sung before may begin their singing with such primitive songs. Birds that are not singers, such as jays and magpies, indulge at times, usually in fall, in primitive song. In contrast to territory songs, these primitive songs are infrequently heard, have no definite form, are not loud, and are not distinctive of species. We can do little more in studying them than to determine which species use them, the season when they do so, and the question of whether young birds or adults are the chief or possibly the only ones to use them.

Song is seasonal, but the particular season, the definite date when it begins or ends, varies greatly with species. Some birds, such as the song sparrow, meadowlark, cardinal, and Carolina wren, sing more or less throughout the year. Others, such as the brown thrasher, rose-breasted grosbeak, and Louisiana water thrush, sing for a short time. Most of our migratory species sing on migration and are singing when they first arrive on the breeding grounds. A few arrive silently and do not begin singing for some days, or even weeks, after their arrival. Songs of some summer residents cease in June or July, while others continue till late August. Certain species commonly revive the song in late summer or fall, after the postnuptial molt. Others do so very rarely or perhaps never. There is a large field for study of this matter and need for prolonged studies through a period of years in numbers of different localities.

In studying the cessation of song after the nesting season, it is not merely enough to record the last date on which a song is heard from a particular species. With a species that is a common breeder and singer in the region of the observer, notes should be made also on the date when the first sign of cessation is noticed; when the species as a whole has ceased singing; and when the last straggler has finally ceased to sing.

Examining records over a period of years shows that there is great variation from year to year. In some years, songs cease early. In others, they are continued to later dates than usual. With species that are rather irregular singers, there is great variation in the volume of song from year to year. Nonpasserine species, such as the cuckoos and the mourning dove, show surprisingly different conditions in different years. Variations in temperature, rainfall, humidity, and food supply all probably have effects on the season of song, but which is the most potent factor is not easily determined.

The manner in which song varies through the day in the height of the season is a matter of considerable interest. As a rule, the greatest amount of singing comes in the early morning and the next greatest in the evening. At times there is considerable singing all through the day. Weather from day to day has something to do with the abundance of song, and the season of the year much more.

Another problem that has been studied a little by a few students is the order in which species begin singing in the early morning and the order in which they cease singing at night. To observe it, one must be up and out where birds are to be found before the first daylight. As a rule, finches, thrushes, and flycatchers begin to sing quite early, warblers a little later, and vireos still more so. There are also differences between birds that inhabit forests and those that live in thickets or open grasslands.

Some birds have special ways of singing in the early morning that differ from daytime singing. This is particularly true of the flycatchers. Many of the flycatchers have songs, known as "twilight songs," that are generally sung between the first beginning of daylight till a short time before sunrise. Twilight songs have been reported for most of the flycatchers but not, to my knowledge, for the olive-sided flycatcher. This bird may have such a song waiting to be discovered and described.

The best known of the twilight songs, and perhaps the most musical of them, is that of the eastern wood pewee. A co-operative study of this song has been made and the results published. This is the first co-operative study of a bird song that has yet been made, and brings to light a great amount of detail about this bird's singing habits and serves as a model for other possible co-operative studies in the future.

Occasional individuals of almost any species of bird may have unusual songs, so different from the normal song of the species that the bird stands out and can be readily identified as an individual. Sometimes the song is so different that it is not recognizable until the bird is seen. The student must depend on chance to hear and study such singers, but they are common enough so that one or more examples can be found nearly every year. How such individuals have come to sing so differently from the rest of their kind is a matter about which we can theorize. Perhaps they are geniuses, improving the song of their species. Perhaps they have inherited this genius from somewhere back in their ancestry. Perhaps they are merely imitating some song or other sound that they heard in early youth.

A question that has been discussed a great deal and is still not definitely settled is that of how young birds get the ability to sing, whether by imitation or heredity. A young bird begins to sing the song of its species. In a majority of cases its song is more or less individual; like that of its species in a general way, but with certain peculiarities that are all its own. It undoubtedly inherited the ability to sing, but it hardly seems as if it could inherit its individual peculiarities. Studies of acquirement of song by young birds in captivity have, in some cases, shown that the young bird inherits its song and in others that it imitates some sound it hears. We may learn much by a study of captive birds, but a number of results of such studies seems to show that when birds are kept in captivity they often produce sounds or songs that are not the original, natural ones. The study of the sounds made by a caged parrot will not teach us much about the sounds its species makes in the wild state. Man inherits the ability to make sounds but has to acquire speech. Foreign-born Americans usually speak with an accent, but their children born in this country do not. So birds, living in nature with their own kind, sing the song of their species, but when brought up in captivity may acquire something else. Probably singing what we have called primitive song is inherited, but singing the normal songs of the species is acquired.

Scientific study of variations in songs can be made only by those who have a good musical ear; who can distinguish between time, pitch, loudness, quality, and phonetics in bird songs, and describe these factors accurately. One who cannot do this can, of course, use any method that appeals to him as helpful in learning to know songs. He may write down catchwords or phrases that seem like the song as he hears it, and if these are helpful to others, there is no reason why they should not be used. But these should not be recorded as if they were scientific descriptions of songs.

Musical notation is fairly accurate, especially with those bird singers that sing largely on the notes of the diatonic scale. But all birds do not do this, nor is the time in bird songs always the same as the standards in man's music. Books have been written that give musical notations for the songs of common birds of eastern United States, and those that prefer this method can avail themselves of these.

Another method, which can record quarter tones or less and time variations not reduced to measures, is in use and has been explained. Its use, recording bird songs in the field, is actually much easier and simpler than musical notation, if one understands it.

For those who possess a good musical ear and wish to try making accurate, scientific descriptions of bird songs and studying variations in bird songs, I would suggest the following procedure. Listen carefully to some comparatively simple bird song and ask yourself questions about it. I would suggest the eastern meadowlark as a good species to start with. How many notes are in the song? Are all these notes the same in the length of time they take? If not, which notes are shorter and which longer? Are the shorter notes just half as long as the longer, or is there some other proportion in length? Next consider pitch. Are all the notes on the same pitch, or are some notes higher or lower than others? Which notes are higher and which lower? How many different pitches are in the song? Suppose there are as many as four, could you number them, making the highest note 1 and the lowest 4? Can you write these numbers in the order in which they occur in the song? For example, a common five-note song might come out 23134 or 13234. Now listen to another meadowlark, or perhaps to a different song from the same bird, and try to determine its time and pitch. If you try this a number of times, you will begin to appreciate how much variation there is in meadowlark songs, and perhaps you will find a fascination in seeing how many variations you can hear and record, or how often you hear the same song you have once recorded from a different meadowlark.

There is not much variation in the loudness of meadowlark songs, but if you try the method on other birds, you may soon find one in which there is, and record which notes are loudest and which soft. Ovenbirds, blackpoll warblers, cardinals, and white-eyed vireos will show interesting variations in loudness.

Quality in sounds is the difference we note in the tones of the different instruments in an orchestra. Bird songs differ in quality. For example, the most noticeable difference to the beginner, in the songs of the robin and the scarlet tanager, is quality. The robin's song is a clear whistle. That of the tanager is a harsh whistle. For other kinds of bird songs, can you write a word or words that describe the quality of its tones? At the present time we cannot describe or measure the quality of a bird song as accurately as we can time and pitch. Some birds change the quality of their songs. One of the characters of the song of the yellow-breasted chat is the change in quality between notes or groups of notes.

A good many bird songs have sounds in them, at the beginnings or ends of notes, that suggest consonants. The recording of these is what I mean by phonetics. Listen to a bird song, and record, in the field, just what the bird seems to say. I do not mean fit some English words to it, but write down such things as "tweet" or "chick" or "wheeoh" or "ayleelo." Some of these consonant sounds are liquids, like *l* or *r,* as we hear them in the songs of the robin and the wood thrush. Others are explosives, like *t* or *ch,* as heard in the songs of such birds as the cardinal and white-eyed vireo. Some sounds are sibilant, like *s* or *z*. If we write vowel sounds in accordance with pitch, *ee* for the highest and *oo* for the lowest, and other vowels in between, we will have a good phonetic rendition of the song.

Call notes and alarm notes should also be studied as well as songs. These are often too short to measure their time, but the pitch can be recorded and they can be written phonetically. It is surprising how many different calls one species of bird may have. Usually one call and one alarm note are the most commonly heard, but when we make intimate studies around a nest, we may hear quite a number more. The common call notes are as useful in identifying species as are the songs, when they are distinctive, but in some cases, such as the warblers, the call notes of most of the species are so much alike that I doubt if any field student could name all the warblers by the "tsick" sounds they produce.

The Food of Birds

A BIRD must necessarily spend a very large part of the time each day in finding food. Civilized man, having solved his food problem in a different manner, often does not realize the conditions of wild creatures that must search for, and find, the food they require daily. The problem is greater for birds than other classes of creatures, because birds require more food in proportion to their size than other animals. Young birds in the nest grow with great rapidity and consume more than their own weight of food each day; food that parents must find in addition to their own requirements.

When we consider all kinds of birds, the variety of food consumed is great. Almost every kind of animal smaller than some bird, except those forms found only in the deep sea, is likely to be the food of some kind of bird. With our smaller songbirds, the chief foods will fall into three groups: seeds, fruits, and insects.

To the mind of the general public, there is often confusion as to the difference between seeds and fruits. The word "nut," for example, is often defined in a crosswood puzzle as "woody fruit," whereas it is not a fruit but a seed. When the difference between fruit and seed is explained, the attitude of the public is still that it makes little difference. But it does make considerable difference, not only to the ornithologist studying bird foods, but to all men concerning their own food requirements and consequent health. An edible fruit contains a large percentage of water, and the percentage of food in it is small. A seed, on the other hand, contains a concentrated food supply, stored there by nature to feed the embryo plant that sprouts from it, but frequently serving as food for some form of animal instead. Seeds contain much food, and fruits little. Food values, however, are not to be measured merely in quantity, but also in quality. Fruits contain the vitamins and minerals necessary for good health, which are not always obtainable from seeds. Therefore, both kinds of foods are important. I am not aware that we have any direct knowledge of the mineral and vitamin requirements of birds, but it is a logical conclusion that they require such things just as much as does man. Probably wild birds get them much more readily than man, for their food is natural and has not been subjected to the various artificial processes that rob natural foods of such things.

Not all songbirds use seed as food, but only those species that have stomachs equipped for grinding seeds when the birds have swallowed small pebbles or grit to aid in the process. Finches and sparrows, game birds and pigeons are examples of birds that eat seeds and digest them in this manner. Some birds, such as chickadees and nuthatches, break up large seeds before swallowing them, but most seedeaters simply swallow seeds whole. Recent observations have shown that some birds that were not suspected of such habits eat seeds, such as the brown thrasher and the myrtle warbler.

The determination of the exact nature of birds' food and the proportion of different foods that are eaten is not an outdoor study but one for the laboratory, for it can be determined accurately only by stomach analysis. On the other hand, the food of any one kind of bird varies greatly, both with the time of year and with localities. Whenever the field student can determine accurately the particular kind of food, it is worth noting. Whether he makes an observation that adds to our knowledge of bird foods or not, he should have a general knowledge of the character of the food of the common birds he observes. Such knowledge will help him find them at various seasons, attract them to feeding areas or sanctuaries, and understand the particular kind of bird and its seasonal occurrence, importance to man, and its general ecological relations.

One who knows the various species of wild plants will often be able to name, by observation, just what kind of seed or fruit a bird eats, but when birds are picking up scattered seeds on the ground, such seeds are usually too small to be determined by field observation. If one is to determine the seeds or fruits that birds eat, it is obvious that he must know plants as well as birds. A knowledge of plants of all kinds will make the outdoor observer a better ornithologist, and a lack of that knowledge will handicap him or narrow the field in which his observations can be useful.

Birds eat seeds to a much greater extent in winter than in summer. A majority of plants produce their seeds in late summer or fall, and these seeds often remain on the plant or on its dried top throughout the winter. Many trees, such as conifers, birches, and tulip trees, carry their seeds, or some of them, all winter, and with others, the seeds are shed in fall but do not sprout till spring, so that birds can find them on the ground in winter. Some seeds, however, ripen in summer and are sometimes eaten by birds at that time. One may frequently see goldfinches eating dandelion seeds in late May or June. The early tree seeds, such as red and silver maples and elm, so far as my experience goes, are not eaten by birds, though the extinct passenger pigeon was reported to eat the seeds of slippery elm.

The study of bird foods has been carried on largely because the economic relations of birds to man are, or are supposed to be, concerned chiefly with their food. For that reason, studies of the food of species of economic importance have been made, whereas studies of a number of quite common birds whose distribution is such that their economic importance is small have been neglected. From the standpoint of pure science, the food of any one bird is as important as that of any other, and every item of food eaten is of equal importance, even though certain ones have no relation to man's welfare.

When birds eat seeds, they are supposedly harmful if the seeds are grain or those of forest trees, but useful if the seeds are those of weeds. As a matter of fact, many of our arguments about economic value or harm of birds are based on fallacious reasoning. In the early days it was desirable to convert people to the idea that songbirds were useful, and scientific studies of bird food were made with that aim in view. Today special groups having strong political influence are trying to have certain types of wild life destroyed and are working the propaganda with that end in view. A few years ago red-winged blackbirds were accused of destroying four million dollars' worth of rice annually, and thousands of birds were destroyed by poison in the breeding season as an experiment in control. But if the four million dollars' worth of rice had remained in the hands of the farmers, instead of going down the crops of the birds, the price of rice would have been lower, and the farmers no richer and perhaps poorer. In fact, only a few years later the government was destroying crops in greater quantities than any blackbird, in order to keep the price up.

In considering weeds and their seeds, the number of seeds produced by each plant is tremendous; enough so that, if all germinated and grew, there would be no room for plants other than weeds. But only a small proportion of them does grow, for only certain places are favorable for their growth, and there is competition between them and other plants for these areas. The matter that determines how many weeds we have is not how many seeds there are, but how much space there is for them to grow and how well the seeds get distributed to these places. The number of seeds destroyed by birds that eat weed seed is not important.

Man, to a large extent, is responsible for the spread of weeds, for wherever he disturbs the soil, in gardening, grading, road work, building, etc., he leaves areas favorable to weed growth, and frequently, after creating these places, neglects them and allows the weeds to grow. Though we still know too little about how weeds spread, it seems quite likely that birds that eat weed seeds actually aid in their spread, breaking up the tops in winter and scattering seeds on the snow or releasing downy seeds to be blown to new locations by the wind. It may be that they do not digest all the seeds swallowed, and thus spread the seeds to new places, as it is well known that they do with the seeds of berries. So it seems likely that those birds supposedly valuable for weed-seed destruction are actually helping in the spread of weeds.

I am not seeking to show that birds are harmful, or to start any further persecution of them, but merely to show that our reasoning on the economic value of birds has not always been sound. I believe that it is time we stopped trying to stress the economic value of birds in order to protect them. The point is that the scientific, educational, recreational, and aesthetic values of birds far exceed the economic, and it is time that we recognized and stressed that point. A large number of men and women in this country have gained a finer, saner happiness and joy in life because there are birds. The number of such people is steadily increasing year by year and has been so increasing for at least fifty years. The development of such recreation is not a mere fad; it has been too steady, too lasting, too ineradicable for that. We no longer need to plead with people to save our birds because they may save them a few sordid dollars; we should plead because they are creatures of beauty and grandeur, because it should be the right of every American who so desires to find them abundantly in and about his home town. Nor is it merely a matter of songbirds. On this basis we can plead as readily for the hawk, the heron, the wild duck, the grouse, the bob-white, and the woodcock. We, the increasing army of bird lovers, have as much right to these creatures alive as the hunters have to them dead. We have as much right to a voice on the various state game commissions as have the so-called sportsmen. How much, you may ask, are birds worth to us in these values? Who can say? There is no unit for the measure of human happiness.

If birds aid in the spread of weed seeds, it is equally true that, when they eat seeds of forest trees, they aid in their distribution. I have made numerous observations that lead me to the belief that the catkins of birch seeds, which are borne on the trees all winter, will not break up and shed their seeds without the aid of birds. I have specimens of ripe catkins that I have had for years, and they will not break when handled, waved in the air, touched with the hands, or even struck forcibly against hard objects. I believe that unless birds break them up, these catkins will remain unopened until the seeds become infertile. Commonly they are broken up by birds in the wintertime and their winged seeds scattered by the wind. The birds that break them are chiefly goldfinches, pine siskins, and redpolls.

Fruits, the chief of which, so far as birds are concerned, are berries, are eaten by many kinds of birds, more kinds than eat seeds, for no special kind of digestive organ is necessary to digest them. It seems as if almost every kind of small bird sooner or later will be detected eating some kind of wild fruit.

Some years ago I occasionally read a newspaper column on nature, the writer of which was nameless but who answered

questions that were sent in. Someone asked him why the majority of wild berries were red in color. The answer was that there
were no more red berries than other colors. I believed that the
answer to that question might not be right, so tested it myself.
I went through my botany and listed all the plants I knew that
had berries for fruit, putting them in columns according to the
color of the berry. My list numbered ninety-seven plants, forty-
six of which had red berries, twenty-seven blue, fourteen black,
eight white, one yellow, and one green. The number of red-
berried plants almost equaled all the other colors combined.

Now it is obvious that the berry-bearing plants have their
seeds spread and their distribution widened largely through
the agency of birds. Berries are almost always some other color
than green when ripe, and are therefore conspicuous and easily
seen against green foliage. It may be that birds do not see all
colors as man does, but it is well known that the hummingbirds
prefer red flowers to all others, and it may be that red is a
conspicuous color to birds in general. Moreover, many of the
blue and black berries turn red first, and it is my observation
that birds eat such berries frequently when in the red stage,
before they are fully ripe. Two of the black berries I listed, the
sassafras and the pokeberry, have thick, fleshy, conspicuous
red stems, so that one gets an impression of red about them,
though the berries are actually black. I do not know that all
the berries I listed are eaten by birds, but a large majority
are. It would seem that red-berried plants are particularly successful in attracting birds to their fruits and consequently getting their seeds distributed widely.

Berries and small fruits differ greatly in the seasons when

Pin cherries are ripe

they are ripe, and there is a succession of them that produces some sort of berry in condition to be eaten by birds in almost every month. Wild strawberries are the first wild fruits to ripen in the Northeast, though mulberries, which are chiefly cultivated, are a close second, and cultivated cherries at about the same time. Shadbush, raspberries, blackberries, wild cherries, blueberries, huckleberries follow through the summer; most of these are enjoyed by man as well as birds. In late summer some of the dogwood berries begin to ripen, and they attract the earlier fall migrants. Wild grape, spicebush, and sassafras come in September, and birds are so fond of the latter two that their berries are gone very soon. Pokeberries are also an attraction at that season. Flowering dogwood is a favorite in October. By November a large number of plants, whose fruits last all winter, are ready. The viburnums, greenbrier, sumacs, poison ivy, red cedar, and on the forest floor the partridge berry and wintergreen, all have berries that last throughout the winter. Birds, however, rarely touch the red-berried sumacs until early spring, when the early robins and bluebirds find them a source of food when the ground is still frozen and earthworms are unobtainable. For eighteen years I lived where bushes of the common privet grew in my yard, covered each winter by berries, but until the great purple finch invasion of 1939 no bird, to my knowledge, ever touched them. At that time, however, the finches stripped the bushes in a day or two. So it may be that berries we think birds never use will prove useful to them under the right circumstances.

There has always been much talk of poisonous berries that birds will not eat. In my own mind I have questioned whether any wild berries really are poisonous. If nature produced a berry so that the seeds it contains might be better distributed by birds, it would seem that poisonous qualities would defeat that purpose. Quite a number of berries and berrylike fruits reputed, in past times, to be poisonous are now known to be harmless or edible, including, for example, the tomato. I have in my notebooks a considerable list of birds I have seen eat the berry of the purple nightshade, which is usually considered to be poisonous. I have been informed that chickens eat these berries daily through their season and suffer no ill effects. Black nightshade also has a reputation for poisonous properties, but its berries are eaten freely by people in some regions. Some berries are thought to be poisonous merely because of their taste. Birds and humans evidently differ at times in their tastes. I have tasted a number of berries that birds eat commonly and men do not, and generally found them either rather tasteless or unpleasant. In the Rocky Mountains, the robins and waxwings are particularly fond of the mountain buffalo berry (*Shepherdia canadensis*). When I ventured to taste one, I found it intensely bitter.

Insects are a major food not only for the smaller songbirds but are used in varying quantities by almost all birds. A few marine birds are not reported to eat insects, but even there the food of most marine birds has not been studied in great detail. When it has, we may find that even they use insects for food at times.

The general popular conception of insects is that they are harmful creatures and that therefore any bird that eats them is useful to man. Actually, many kinds of insects are harmless, and some, chiefly because they destroy harmful insects, are considered useful. Since birds are valuable to man aesthetically and, in my opinion, of greater real value for this reason than any other, insects are useful because they are birds' food.

The general public misunderstands somewhat the interrelations of living things, such as the relations between birds and insects. But the proper place for the discussion of this matter is under ecology rather than here. It might be just as well, however, to mention that in nearly every case where insects become very destructive it is due to something that man has done. Native insects do not reach destructive numbers in natural areas, where the balance between them, their food supply, and their enemies is maintained. Birds, being enemies of insects, are part of the natural balance, and their place in keeping insects down to normal is important. There has been a tendency among entomologists to minimize this importance and to fight insects by methods that destroy the balance. I believe that we shall never get control over insects until we recognize all the factors and re-establish, as far as possible, the natural conditions.

The study of the insect food of birds is best made by stomach analysis, which shows just what insects, and what proportions of each species, each kind of bird eats. But there are some things that stomach analysis cannot tell us and that field observers can find out by careful observation. Stomach analysis can tell us how many insects can be in a bird's stomach at one time, but just how fast it digests these insects, how many it eats in a day or a season, or how many it feeds to its young when in or just out of the nest are not so easily determined.

On the latter points we have obtained most of our data from field observation.

Exact identification of the kinds of insects eaten by a particular bird requires a knowledge of insects greater than most field ornithologists have. It would be well for those ornithologists who wish to study this subject to obtain a general knowledge of insects and add to it at every opportunity. In the study of the food of our smaller land birds, insects and plants are the most important groups for the student to know.

With our larger birds, food covers a number of other animal groups. Rodents and other small mammals are food for hawks, owls, and some others. Fish, frogs, salamanders, reptiles, spiders, centipedes, crabs, worms, mussels, snails, and other shellfish are foods for various kinds of land, shore, or water birds. Every now and then someone contributes a little more to our knowledge through an observation in the field: a black-crowned night heron swallows a young mallard; a spotted sandpiper catches a small fish; crows feed for weeks on fresh-water mussels in the bottom of a drained reservoir; a hermit thrush feeds its young on salamanders; a catbird eats a luna moth, first removing its wings; a robin swallows swallowtail butterflies, wings and all; these and many similar observations are being constantly made, sometimes telling us what the birds eat, and at other times how they do it. The field for observations on food and feeding habits seems inexhaustible.

A sparrow hawk captures a grasshopper

Ecology

ANYONE with a fair knowledge of common birds knows that he must go to special places to find most kinds of birds. Bitterns, rails, and marsh wrens live in the marshes. Thrushes and ovenbirds are found mainly in the woods. Field sparrows occur on dry bushy hillsides, and vesper sparrows in grassy meadows. Each species has a particular sort of place to live and, at least in the season of nesting, is found only there. Even in migrations and in winter, birds are more or less confined to particular kinds of places, and we will not look for horned larks in the forest, nor for warblers on the sea beach.

If we stop to think about it, we will realize that the abundance of a particular species breeding in our vicinity is determined by the area of the habitat it chooses in that vicinity. This is not true of a species that is out of its normal range, however. There is an abundance of the right habitat for cardinals and mockingbirds in New England, for example, but the location is too far north for such birds to be common. But if we appreciate the differences in habitats, we will find that a species is just about as common as the occurrence of its habitat permits. Species that range over a wide variety of habitats, such as the robin, are quite common, whereas species, such as the worm-eating warbler, that require a very special habitat, found only in a few places, are scarce.

The relation of birds to habitats is a large part of the ecology of birds, for ecology treats of the relations of life to environment. For the bird, we must consider not only the particular habitat required, but also the things within that habitat that furnish it food; the conditions that favor breeding, a nesting site and nesting materials; the rivals of that bird for food and nesting site; and the enemies or conditions that may destroy it. Weather conditions must also be considered, for it is largely the occurrence of favorable or unfavorable weather that limits the range of a species. If we would know much of the ecology of birds, we must know much more than just the birds themselves. We must know both the plant and animal life in practically all of their forms: the water, soil, air, weather, and geology. In fact, it is probably true that no one person is completely equipped to make a thorough and complete study of ecology, even in a single habitat. Complete ecological studies would require co-operative work on the part of a number of different people, but many of us can contribute to ecological knowledge from the standpoint that we do know well.

In the first place, it is fundamental that animal life depends upon plant life. Green plants manufacture foods, but animals must either eat plant food directly or feed upon other animals

Wood ducks in their habitat

that do depend directly on plants. The manufacture of food by plants, and its use by animals, is one part of the most fundamental principle of ecology, the cycle of carbon; the other part being the transference of oxygen from plant to animal, and of carbon dioxide from animal to plant, through the air. Through this process, which is too well known to need detailed explanation here, we can understand that not only are animals dependent on green plants, but green plants upon animals.

Plants are dependent, first of all, on five things: soil, water, and air, which are kinds of matter, and light and heat, which are kinds of energy. The character of the soil and the amount of water in it differ in different localities. The amount of light and heat varies in a single region, according to topography; that is, it is greatest on a slope facing south and least on one facing north. These factors of difference in topography can be referred to as exposure. Therefore, we may conclude that the kinds of plants that grow in any one locality are determined by the soil, moisture, and exposure of that locality.

Over any area where these three requirements are practically uniform, we will find the plants, under natural conditions, uniform also. Such an area is what we refer to as a habitat. Not only are the species of plants uniform, but the animal life also, including the birds. A habitat, therefore, is determined by uniform conditions of soil, moisture, and exposure.

In nature we practically never get absolute uniformity. A sidehill, for example, has that type of soil, moisture, and exposure that is required for a forest of maple and beech. But in a few places on the sidehill are rock outcrops, where the soil is thinner. In other spots are springs which increase the moisture. In such spots the plants will be different over a small area, and perhaps even the trees. Such places will be of particular interest to the botanist and plant ecologist, but only occasionally will they cause enough difference to change the character of the bird life. There can be such differences, however. I have seen a maple-beech forest that contained a scattering amount of hemlock, and where springs occurred on the hillside there would be a small hemlock grove. Where these groves were found, there would be likely to be colonies of blackburnian or magnolia warblers, or both, where these species were rare or absent in the more normal forest. In other places, where a big tree had died or been blown over, light, penetrating to the forest floor, caused a dense growth of forest shrubs and young trees, and this created favorable conditions for black-throated blue and hooded warblers.

This last brings out the point that the amount of light and heat is not determined by exposure only, but also by the plants and trees already on the area. Within a mature forest the light and heat are less and the moisture greater than on an area of the same exposure where there is no forest. Forest floor plants have been shown to grow better in shade than in direct sunlight. So when the forest is removed, these plants disappear and others of more weedy growth come in, and the habitat has changed. All animal life, including birds, changes when the forest is cut down.

In any habitat, the green plants manufacture the fundamental food, but there are other plants that are not green.

These plants live either as parasites on other plants or some-times on animals, or as saprophytes, living on dead and decay-ing plant or animal matter. The bacteria and fungi are groups of such plants. In some cases these saprophytes have a relation to bird life, at least indirectly, fleshy fungi being frequently used for food by the spruce partridge, but they have an ex-ceedingly important relation to the whole habitat. They cause the decay of all the dead material in the forest; the logs, branches, twigs, and leaves that fall to the ground would not decay without the action of saprophytes. Because they do decay, the nitrogenous matter of which they are composed is returned to the soil, thus keeping the soil in constant good condition for the growth of plants and consequently the life of animals. The plant life of the habitat then may be divided into three groups in relation to their manner of obtaining food: the green plants, the parasites, and the saprophytes.

In a similar manner we may class the animals in four groups, according to the foods they eat and their manner of obtaining them. These are the herbivores, predators, parasites, and scav-engers. The herbivores feed upon plants; the predators kill and eat other animals; the parasites take their living from other animals also, not killing them directly, and often not at all, but sometimes causing the ultimate death of their hosts; the scav-engers eat dead animals or plant matter, occupying a place somewhat parallel to that of the saprophytes among plants.

There are herbivores, predators, etc., not only among the vertebrate animals, but also among insects and other groups. Among the higher animals one cannot say that a particular species is always one or the other of those classifications. Such a bird as the crow may be predator, herbivore, or scavenger, according to what it happens to feed upon. Very few birds, if any, are entirely predator or herbivore, but mostly a little of both. In invertebrate animals, most of the species are entirely one or another.

The term "predator" has been applied recently, particularly in wildlife management, to mean animals that are predatory on game, a less objectionable word to take the place of the term "vermin." But strictly speaking, predators are not merely carnivorous mammals and birds, but will include insectivorous birds, ground beetles, dragonflies, spiders, salt-water snails, starfish, and many others.

There sometimes seems to be a difficulty distinguishing between parasite and predator. Both live on other animals, but the predator kills directly for its food, and kills again when hunger comes. The parasite may never kill its host and may live on that host all its life. But there are some cases where there may be some doubt. We would commonly consider a mosquito a parasite, though it does not live continually on one host, and in fact may live its life successfully without attacking any animal. I have seen a certain small leech clinging to a large snapping turtle, the leech unquestionably a parasite, somewhat similar to the mosquito in its way of living. I have seen the same kind of leech kill a small sunfish in a minute or so; under such circumstances, a voracious predator.

Within the habitat, all plants and animals live together, the green plants making the food, the herbivores eating it and being in turn preyed upon by both predators and parasites. The saphrophytes and scavengers clear up the dead material.

In a natural habitat, this goes on without great change year after year. Insects are much more numerous than birds, and small birds more numerous than the large predatory ones. Mammals, in general, are in small numbers, but the most numerous are the small rodents that are chiefly herbivores.

Now among these various organisms the rate of reproduction varies tremendously. Deer, bear, and other large animals have but a few young at a time, and then not more than once a year. Songbirds may nest two or three times in a season and have three to five or six young in each brood. Meadow mice may have young every three weeks and six to eight in each litter. Insects may lay several hundred to a thousand eggs and have a whole life cycle in so short a time as a week or ten days. A big forest tree may produce thousands of seeds each year, each one a potential big forest tree. But the numbers of plants and animals do not change greatly from year to year.

Now if we stop to think about it, we can see why this is so. The different animals do not increase permanently, though some kinds reproduce in large numbers, because there are predators and parasites and many dangers in life; in short, because of the process going on continually, which we know as the struggle for existence. The large, powerful animals, with few or no enemies and few other dangers, have only a few young each year. The smaller animals, preyed upon by many other creatures, have a large number of young. In other words, the principle is that *rate of reproduction of any one species is adjusted by nature to the keenness of its struggle for existence.*

Theoretically, if the conditions in the habitat were entirely uniform, the numbers of individuals of each species would remain the same, and this would also be true of the proportion between predators, herbivores, green plants, etc. But conditions are only approximately uniform. In fact, the lack of uniformity begins, first of all, with the weather. This, as we know, changes continually from year to year, changing the amount of water, light, and heat that influence the green plants directly and, therefore, less directly, every living thing in the habitat. Some winters are long and cold. Others are short and mild. Snow is deep in one year and almost lacking in another. The growing season, between latest and earliest killing frosts, varies greatly in length. Summers may be hot or comparatively cool, and exceedingly dry or wet. All these things affect the life of the habitat and cause variation from year to year. With such creatures as insects, with a high rate of reproduction and a great number of enemies, the fluctuations in numbers may be very great. With rodents, which have the highest reproduction rate among warm-blooded animals, the fluctuation is considerable. With songbirds it is often quite noticeable. Yet each species, under natural conditions, holds its own and, if it becomes scarce for a few years, returns to normal and perhaps exceptional abundance in a few years more. The process is what is known as the "balance of nature," each species dependent in various ways on the others with which it is associated, which constitute its food, its rivals, or its enemies.

When we begin to think about this, a natural question comes up: What about the large predator that has no larger ones to prey upon it? Eagles, bears, mountain lions, and wolves exist in smaller numbers than others, yet they have no enemies to keep their numbers down. Why shouldn't they increase? The trouble here is that we have been thinking of the struggle for existence as just a matter of enemies, whereas it is also a matter of food. The ultimate predator requires more food than smaller organisms. If its numbers increase for a time, individuals become rivals of each other for food, and food, especially in winter, becomes scarce and hard to get. Those individuals that are less successful in obtaining it soon become weak from lack of food, and starvation follows. If large predators have become numerous and reduce the numbers of the herbivores on which they prey, then they too are reduced in numbers, and the herbivores will begin to increase again. I am speaking here of entirely natural conditions, which do not include man, with his high-powered rifles, traps, and poisoned baits. When man inserts his power with such things, the balance of nature is no longer maintained.

If we choose to study the ecology of birds, we want to learn not only which species live in which habitats, but also how numerous they are in that habitat; what other things are their enemies, their rivals, and their food; what conditions are necessary for their successful reproduction. To find out about all these things, we must know much more than just the birds, for the other animals and the plants all have something to do with the birds' lives. The ecologist, though his chief interest may be birds, must be something of an all-around naturalist.

We learn that a certain organism is the food of a certain bird, and immediately the things that affect that organism, that constitute its food or make the conditions under which it lives, become important to the bird. For example, when I watched a redstart in the forest capturing and eating fungus gnats, I noted that the gnats were swarming about a certain spot. In fact, they were swarming about a fungus, a common species, known as *Collybia platyphylla*. In turn, this fungus was growing on a decaying maple log. The gnats were food for the redstart, the fungus food for the gnats, and the log food for the fungus. So each of these organisms was of importance to the redstart. All through the habitat, certain things are of direct importance to the various birds, and they, in turn, depend on other organisms. We do not know all of the details of such interrelations; in fact, we know very few of them, so that, of all the various organisms that make up the habitat, we cannot say that any one is of no importance to bird life.

Throughout nature we find many cases where one organism eats another, and that one a third, etc. Such things are known as food chains—the redstart, gnat, fungus, and log, and other similar relationships. There are innumerable such chains if we can discover them. The beginning of a complete chain must be a green plant; for example, the tree that became a decayed log. The end of the chain is not necessarily the bird, but some enemy that destroys the bird, or still farther. The end of the chain, in other words, is an ultimate predator.

The world is full of plants. There are great numbers especially when we consider the microscopic ones. There must be such numbers to feed the many animals. Insects and other small animals are also extremely numerous. As we go up the scale to the vertebrates, the numbers become less, till we finally reach the very small numbers of the ultimate predators. This is known as the pyramid of numbers; the greatest numbers at the base and the fewest at the peak.

The least bittern in a cattail marsh

Each species of bird lives in its own particular kind of habitat and there fills its place or niche. In some cases we find the bird especially adapted to that habitat. A rail has large feet, which help it to walk over soft mud of the marsh in which it lives without sinking in. It has a narrow body, which it can compress to still narrower dimensions, enabling it to squeeze between the reeds or cattails of the marsh. Its coloring is undoubtedly protective, striped on the back, as seen from above, and barred on the lower sides, as seen from one side, and these markings blend with the lights and shadows of the reeds and grasses. It instinctively hides among such vegetation when danger approaches, and in such places it is difficult to see. The bill of the more typical rail is long, slightly curved down, and adapted for probing in the mud for its food. The rail is a specialized form and would find difficulty living anywhere but in a marsh.

The red-winged blackbird also lives in a marsh but has few, if any, of these adaptations. The male is not in the least protectively colored, and the coloration of the female would fit with other types of vegetation as well as with the marsh. The feet and bill are not essentially different from those of birds that live in other habitats. It would seem that this bird could live equally well in a group of trees as in a marsh, but, though it often perches in trees, it does not live or nest there.

The warblers are a group of birds that are much alike in shape, size, and characters of bill and feet. Yet the habitats they live and nest in vary considerably. Some nest on the ground, some in bushes, and some in trees. It would seem as if a chestnut-sided warbler would be equally successful nesting in a tree of the forest as in a low bush in a thicket. A black-throated green warbler might nest as readily in a bush in a thicket as in the hemlock trees of a forest. But the birds do not so change their habitats. This is evidently due to inherited habit, or instinct to select a particular habitat. That is, certain species are psychologically adapted to a particular habitat, though physically they might be fitted to a variety of habitats. It can hardly be doubted that even the specialized species, such as the rail, select their habitats by instinct. This instinct is the controlling factor that determines the habitat in which a species lives. Since it is the area of its habitat that under natural conditions controls the abundance of a species, each species is limited in its numbers by its instinct.

There is, however, considerable difference in species as to the extent to which this instinct limits them. The robin may live in the forest or the orchard or the shade trees of a village street. Lawns have evidently made a better feeding place for the robin than natural areas, as it is evidently easier to obtain its earthworm food there than elsewhere. It seems probable that there are more robins today than before the country was settled.

In contrast to the robin, the Louisiana water thrush is quite restricted in the areas where it can live. It requires a brook or a swamp in forested areas, and when man drains or fills in the swamp or removes the forest and civilizes the brook, the bird can no longer live there. The areas where it can live have become smaller. It is probable that there are smaller numbers of Louisiana water thrushes today than when the country was first settled.

The instinct of the robin for its original habitat, probably forest, was not so strong but that it could be modified to suit changes in conditions. I am inclined to think that the ability of a species to modify instincts is an indication that it has a greater degree of intelligence than the species that lacks that ability. Quite a number of species in America have modified nesting habits to fit changes brought about by man; particularly the barn and cliff swallows, the chimney swift, the nighthawk, and the phoebe. In the West the dipper has, in some localities at least, undergone such a change, nesting, as does the phoebe, on beams under bridges. Unlike the phoebe, however, its nest is always near running water, as its habits and food require that.

Although I mentioned the red-winged blackbird as a bird that lives in marshes, there are indications in some regions that certain individuals are changing their habits and nesting in the tall grass of fields that are by no means swampy in character.

There are times when certain requirements in a bird's habitat limit its distribution, but seem, from a human standpoint, quite unnecessary. David Lack, in England, who first called attention to the importance of this instinct to select a habitat, uses the tree pipit as an illustration. Although the bird lives in grassland and nests in the grass, it requires one or more trees on which to alight after a song flight, and its instinct in this matter is so strong that it cannot nest in areas where there is no tree or at least a pole that can be used for this purpose. I believe that in America the ruffed grouse will not be found in woodlands where the old logs have all been removed, for its instinct requires a log on which to drum. At least I know of areas on private lands where hunting is not permitted where the forest, in all other particulars, would seem to be right for ruffed grouse, but both old logs and the birds are absent. I know of other areas, some of them not protected against hunting, where there are still plenty of logs and also ruffed grouse.

Some of these illustrations bring out the point that dead logs, dead trees, and decaying things are part of the habitat, important to certain birds and probably to many other animals. Man thinks of such things as useless and considers that cleaning up a forest area of such things is an improvement. But ecological studies show that every natural factor in the habitat is of some importance to the organisms that live there. Since there are few if any organisms in the habitat that are not important to birds, then these things are all important to birds.

Nature is in a constant state of change. Usually these changes are very slow, so that we cannot observe them directly in a lifetime. But we can observe areas in different stages of the changes, and from these observations infer what is taking place. For example, there is the well-known recession of glaciers that once covered the northern half of North America. Such recession is probably still going on, and if so, our climate is gradually getting warmer. In the Glacier National Park one may observe various stages in the recession. If one walks along a trail that goes from some high mountain pass down a stream valley, he observes first steep, rocky mountain sides, snowbanks, and glaciers. Then there are glacial lakes, usually a chain of them, each with its terminal moraine and a waterfall. These lakes, as we travel downward, are gradually shallower. They tend to fill up with sediment as time goes on. Farther down, willow

bushes are growing on the old moraines, till, on the lower remains of old lakes, there are willow thickets, flat areas covered
with dense willow growth, which we can recognize as the remains of a former glacial lake. Then we begin to notice here
and there small spruce trees growing up among the willows.
The numbers of spruces gradually increase, and where they are
dense enough to form a small grove, we may find dead remains
of willow bushes beneath them. Still farther along, the spruces
are more numerous and older and of larger size, till we finally
come upon mature spruce forest, covering a flat area, where
once, many years ago, there was a glacier.

So the gradual change that has been going on has caused
changes in habitats, and each habitat has its own distinct kinds
of living creatures. From the bird standpoint, we may have
noticed, as we progressed, that there were gray-crowned rosy
finches, pipits, and white-tailed ptarmigan about the glaciers.
But in the willow thickets were Lincoln and white-crowned
sparrows and pileolated warblers, whereas in the spruce forest
were golden-crowned kinglets, Audubon's warblers, creepers,
and Franklin's grouse. Evidently, with the slow, gradual, geological changes, the bird life has also changed. Such a change is
known in ecology as a succession.

There are numerous successions of a geological sort, for such
changes are taking place practically everywhere. Successions
that we can observe more readily come about when conditions
are changed suddenly. Such changes are natural ones, when a
landslide or a heavy windfall occurs, but more commonly there
are artificial ones, when man changes conditions by cutting
forests, causing forest fires, draining marshes, etc. One of the

commonest of successions comes when man cuts down the forest and leaves nature to reforest it naturally. The organisms of the forest, whether birds, animals, or plants of the forest floor, disappear, and other plants come in and form a thicket, which is soon occupied by thicket-dwelling birds. If the forest was one of broad-leaved trees, it usually reforests by sprouting, but if the forest is an evergreen one of pine or spruce, reforestation is slower and by seedlings. Sometimes a forest of evergreens is followed by broad-leaved trees, but when fire follows the cutting, temporary, short-lived trees or shrubs seed in rather than the species of the original forest.

All of these changes in vegetation make a corresponding change in bird life. There is still too little known about these changes and plenty of opportunity for observation and research for those who have the knowledge and ability to do it. In the thicket stage, such birds as field sparrows, yellowthroats, towhees, catbirds, thrashers, and indigo buntings are likely to occupy the area. As the thicket grows up to forest, these birds gradually disappear, and the true forest birds, such as thrushes, red-eyed vireos, and warblers, gradually come in. Each species appears when conditions that it requires to live and nest there occur. Bird life is generally abundant in a thicket a few feet high. It is my experience that as the thicket gets higher and the small trees close their crowns the bird life decreases, and for a time, until the forest grows taller, there are very few birds. As the forest grows taller, the birds increase in numbers and also in number of species. When the forest reaches maturity, the number of birds and species has reached a maximum.

In a field or meadow, provided that the conditions over the

area are uniform, the number of birds living there will be in proportion to its area, and this probably also applies to the thicket. But when, by closing of crowns or succession of permanent trees over temporary shrubs, the thicket becomes forest, the number of birds thereafter is determined by its volume. That is, the taller the trees grow, the more room there is for birds to live. These points, however, should be checked by careful field work. They may not apply in all kinds of forest. There may be differences, as when a forest is cut and grows back by sprouting, or when an old abandoned field grows into a thicket of sumac, bayberry, and cedar and finally becomes forest again. A field planted to young pine and gradually growing to forest size represents another case, and a burned-over former spruce forest, grown up to aspen and pin cherry, still another.

Areas where the moisture is greater generally support more birds. Swamps and marshes have exceedingly abundant bird life. The borders of lakes and streams have more bird life than the interiors of forests, and this is true also where forests border on meadows, thickets, or other more open places. Some of these conditions, however, are artificial ones, brought about by man's changes of nature. It is perhaps best for us to determine how and in what numbers birds occur in natural areas, and then find out to what extent artificial conditions change these areas. A forest, with its undergrowth of forest floor plants removed by cutting, fire, or grazing, will not support nearly as many birds as a natural forest. In other cases, artificial conditions may increase bird life or at least increase some species of birds. With the cutting of forests and clearing of lands, fields, meadows, and thickets have increased, and the species that live in them are undoubtedly more numerous today. A hundred years ago the chestnut-sided warbler was considered to be one of the rare species. Today, with the increase of thickets and low shrubs, such as it prefers for nesting, it has become one of the commonest of warblers.

Determining how many birds can live on an area in the breeding season is important ecological work that can be done accurately only by those who have a good field knowledge of birds. In the first place, such counts should be done by habitats. Some counts made in the past covered varied areas, where fields, orchards, thickets, and wood lots all occurred. While they were interesting, they gave indefinite results, which could not be used to predict the bird life of other areas. Areas chosen for counting birds should either be all in one habitat, or, if covering two or more habitats, the counts should be kept separate in each, and the area of each computed.

In some of the counts that have been made recently, it would seem that participants picked out areas especially favorable to bird life, the idea being, apparently, to see who could find the greatest number of birds on a given area. But it is just as important for us to know how many birds live on an area that is average or least favorable.

Counts are made in various ways. Going over a particular area several times in a season, using every way to find all the birds living on that area, would seem the best way to get results on a single locality. Care should be taken not to count the same bird twice. Some counts have been made by counting singing males and considering that each such male represents a pair. It is not certain that this is true, for there are some unmated birds. Also, with a number of species, the males cease to sing in some parts of the nesting cycle. In fact, with some birds, the brown thrasher, for example, a count of singing males would quite certainly be a count of how many males are not mated. I believe, however, that those species that cease to sing in part of the nesting cycle are the ground, bush, and hole-nesting species, and that practically all tree nesters, especially in forest areas, sing throughout the cycle. This is fortunate in counting birds of a dense, mature forest. How anyone could find and count the treetop birds in such an area if they did not sing is hard to conceive.

Singing ceases with most species as summer advances, and birds become less in evidence during the time of molt. After the nesting is over, there should be more birds in an area than before, for the young are out of the nests. But finding those birds is another matter. In June, in the proper kind of forest area, ovenbirds, for example, are very common. We hear the songs in many places and frequently see the birds. But in August one may travel through miles of such woodland and often see none at all, or will feel lucky if he sees one or two. In forest areas, in my experience, it is not possible to make accurate counts of bird life after about July 15, and it is still better to confine counting to June.

Up to the present time, people have been making counts of birds on small areas, and these counts show fairly well how many birds can occur on a given area. But whether it shows how many do occur if the count made should be applied to a larger area may be doubted. It seems to me that the chief value of counts of breeding birds is to obtain something that can be applied to similar areas, and thus give us some idea of the number of birds in a larger region. That is, we should use counts on smaller areas to estimate the numbers of birds on larger ones. Such a thing has been tried. The results give much smaller totals over the whole area than counts of many small areas would lead us to expect. But the area estimated included a large percentage of second-growth forest on the drier hilltops, where bird life was scarce. No one picking out a single area on which to make a bird count would be likely to choose an area like that. But the point is that there are such areas, and they must be taken into consideration if we want to get an accurate idea of the actual number of birds in large areas.

In the vicinity of civilization, areas of wild land are small and more or less broken up, or their conditions changed by grazing, brush cutting, fire, and similar things. Some areas are especially favorable for bird life, and the birds concentrate there. They are especially numerous where the forest and open meet. Picking a single highly favorable area and making a count on it give high results. In more remote regions, where large areas of natural, wild land occur, the birds are more uniform in distribution, and counts on one area are more nearly applicable to much larger similar areas. In such a case, one does not pick a spot especially favorable to birds, but makes counts on portions of the area, wherever they happen to come. It is my opinion that the most accurate results will be obtained not by laying out plots, but by counting birds of certain strips that cross the whole area. If the land is hilly, these strips should be at right angles to the slope. This saves time in laying out the area, for one may simply pace a straight line and record all birds within a certain distance of that line on either side. The distance is determined by the conditions and distances to which one can see or hear birds and identify them accurately. Knowing the length of the line and the distances determined, one can compute easily the acreage covered.

The significant thing about counts like these, in my experience, is that, when made in the same habitat where there are essentially uniform conditions, the counts show very nearly the same numbers of birds for a given area and practically the same proportions of species. After making a number of such counts, one can tell pretty definitely how the others will go. We soon have a basis for determining the number of birds of each species per unit of area. If we know the total acreage of that habitat, we can estimate with reasonable accuracy how many birds are on the area. Such an estimate, however, will hold true only for the year in which it is made, for there are evidently cyclical changes in numbers and proportions of species through a period of years. It would take repeated counts for a number of years to determine the average year.

Comparatively little has been done in the study of the ecology of each separate species. The subject is a large one, and it is to be expected that no one can cover it completely by his own observations alone. But we can do much more than has been done.

We wish to know about any one species not only what habitat it lives in and how abundant it is in that habitat, but what are its relations to all the other species in that habitat. We want to know what are its foods and how these vary at different seasons. We want to know its enemies, its rivals for food and for nesting sites; its nesting locality and nesting materials, and any special requirements its instincts need in the matter of courtship, singing, nesting, or other habits. We want to know its relationship to weather conditions; the extent to which sudden storms or changes in temperature may affect it. All of these things in the habitat that it requires directly are primary factors in its environment.

Now these primary factors depend, themselves, on other things. An insect that is food for a certain bird may require some special plant. That plant, therefore, is important to the bird, not primarily, but secondarily. That plant, in turn, is dependent on certain conditions of soil, moisture, or exposure, which therefore also become important to the bird. Thus we can see that any species of bird is dependent on factors in its environment that are primary, secondary, tertiary, or even more remotely removed. But they are all more or less important.

The importance of different factors varies. That is, suppose a bird eats several different species of insects; some are eaten in large numbers and others only occasionally. Some are so seldom eaten that if they were not present it would not affect the bird adversely. We can therefore classify the primary factors of a bird's environment as major or minor. In this connection we should bear in mind that a major secondary factor would be more important to the bird than a minor primary one. In other words, the plant or tree that feeds those insects which the bird eats daily and in large quantities is more important than some insect which the bird eats only occasionally.

Insects vary greatly in numbers from year to year, and for that reason those that are major factors in one year may be only minor in another. But there always seem to be plenty of insects of one kind or another to furnish the food necessary for birds, at least in natural areas. Probably the real importance of an insect as food is not so much a particular species as a family or other group. The spanworms (*Geometridae*), for example, are a family of moths whose larvae are always abundant in forest areas and a major factor in the food of many forest-dwelling birds. But which species in that family is the major factor varies in different years. Probably caterpillars of any one species are as acceptable to birds as another. The same seems to be true in different species of cutworm moths.

Ecology is a very large subject. No one can know it all. If we study bird ecology, we are bound to have to consider the ecology of other organisms as well. But the ecology of birds and the higher animals is more complicated than that of lower ones. The food of the higher organisms is varied, but with most of the invertebrates the food is simple, often confined to a single species. So when we attempt to study ecology, primarily from the standpoint of birds, we are attempting one of the most highly complicated phases of the subject.

But the study of ecology is important. If we would have wild birds in numbers or have any particular wild species, we must have the right environment in which they can live. If we desire to save our bird life for the future, so that people in our country a hundred or a thousand years from now may still have our varied bird life to enrich their lives, we must not destroy the environment in which these birds live. We must know the factors of that environment that are necessary. In other words, ecology is the chief factor in the conservation of wildlife for the future.

The Problems of Conservation

A GREAT deal has been written about conservation of various kinds, but whenever there is an attempt to put all the kinds of conservation into one publication, it has required a number of different authors. Often these different authors, writing about different phases of conservation, are contradictory to each other in many of their statements. Yet they all appear in the same book, and each person reads the account of the kind of conservation that interests him most and does not notice the contradiction. So we go on, each talking about conservation in his own narrow field and none of us getting much wiser, or trying to get rid of the contradictions, and conservation goes on being one thing to one man and quite a different thing to another.

The word "conservation" as we now use it began with the foresters, and they meant it to express the wise use of natural resources, especially applying it, of course, to forests. In the early days we wasted our forests, the idea being to cut the trees and make use of the wood as quickly and cheaply as possible. Our wood supply seemed inexhaustible, and we looked upon it as a spendthrift would look upon a large sum of money to which he had become heir. Later, when our forests began to disappear rapidly, we went to the opposite extreme. We must save our forests and not cut them. Big trees are beautiful things. Let us keep them and look at them. To many people, still, this is the chief goal of conservation. But to the forester, this is no more conservation than wasteful cutting. Trees grow old and die, fall to the ground, lie on the forest floor, and decay. Yet we need wood, and the procedure of reserving a forest is also wasteful. The reservationist is not like the spendthrift, but his opposite, the miser, storing his hoard where it is useless but where he can look at it and gloat over his possessions.

Trees grow. The amount of wood that grows each year in a given forest can be measured. That amount is known as the sustained annual yield, and the equivalent of that amount can be cut and used each year without destroying the forest. To the forester, the forest is like a sum of money, neither to be wasted nor hoarded, but invested wisely. The sustained annual yield is the interest it bears. That sort of use was the original meaning of conservation as applied to natural resources.

When we discuss conservation of living things of no economic use, this forestry conception does not apply. We may conserve them because they are economically valuable, alive, as they are; or because they are wild living things that we appreciate and have no good reason to destroy. This is largely the kind of conservation that applies to birds.

The sportsman's conservation is, or should be, like that of the forester. There can be such a thing as a sustained annual yield in game to guide sportsmen as to how many individuals of a particular kind of game can be killed in a year in a given area without reducing the numbers in years to come. In a good many states, however, the number of hunting licenses that may be issued is limited only by the number of citizens that want them, and there is often not sufficient game in the state for each licensed sportman to kill the number he is allowed legally. This is not conservation, and it is hard to see how we are going to have more game in the future under such practices. The number of sportsmen in many states is increasing, and the amount of game—in fact, the area in which game can live—is decreasing. This comes about through a political arrangement by which the money for salaries of game wardens is derived directly from money received for hunting licenses. Under such circumstances the number of hunting licenses cannot be limited. Of course it is good democracy to allow every citizen who desires to hunt the right to do so, but we cannot increase the amount of game automatically with the number of licenses. With an introduced bird, such as the pheasant, we can liberate more with the increase of hunters, but there is a limit even then. Raising pheasants in captivity, just to be liberated and killed, is no more wildlife conservation than raising vegetables in a garden is forestry. Were it not for a large area of private lands where hunting is not allowed in our thickly populated states, some of our game birds in those states would be on the verge of extinction now. When the day comes that we limit hunting licenses and are as careful about the fitness of a man to go hunting as about his fitness to drive a car, we may be able to practice conservation of game.

The economic value of birds other than game has been discussed, and emphasized, and disbelieved by a few. It is actually rather a difficult thing to gauge. A bird eats whatever it can get, at any time it can find it, without regard to whether the thing it eats is useful or harmful to man. We analyze the food it has eaten and determine what percentage is doing us good, what percentage harm, and what neutral. But actually that question is not determined entirely by the food, but by the circumstances under which it is eaten, and that we often do not know. We condemn a bird for eating grain, when that grain may have been spilled along a roadside, where it would have been wasted. We praise the bird that eats insects, forgetting that some of those insects are useful and others harmless creatures whose only plant food is some kind of weed.

The fact is that we want to conserve our bird life, not because it is economically valuable, but because it is beautiful and inspiring. For such a reason, we would save not only warblers and thrushes but also herons and hawks. To one who argues that this is not practical, I would answer that we spend large sums of money for art museums and symphony orchestras and flower gardens, and these are not practical either. But they are beautiful and increase human happiness. We would condemn the man who would turn his city property into a sordid slum, merely because it is cheaper and brings a quicker return. We should likewise condemn those who destroy wild beauty spots that are homes of wild life, and turn them into ugly wastes where wild creatures cannot live, because by so doing they see a quick way to make a few more dollars. I know a desolate area of weedy sand where a few years ago there was a beautiful forest, full of bird life and wild rare plants. But the gravel beneath the forest had a commercial value. I know of numerous similar things here in my own region, and nature lovers in other spots doubtless know of many more. In many cases the commercial materials could have been obtained elsewhere, and the beauty spots could have been saved. But to men so minded, it was cheapest and easiest to commit the destruction. We who know these natural beauties must continually keep on insisting on the value of them, on their great contribution to human happiness, on the increase of the value in future years, as more and more people come to see that their lives can be wiser, saner, and happier when they have beautiful nature to look upon and contemplate.

In a natural area where there is an abundance of both birds and insects, the insects are only potentially harmful. Their natural enemies, including birds, keep them in check. If something took the birds away the insects would make trouble, for their rate of reproduction is very great. But as long as nature controls, that high rate of reproduction is merely adjusted to their exceedingly keen struggle for existence. Actually, under natural conditions, these insects are useful, for they furnish the main food of birds.

The general public thinks about insects chiefly as harmful creatures, without which the world would be better off. Their chief attitude is that the only good bug is a dead bug. So they step on the big ground beetle that scurries across the sidewalk, or smash the little lady beetle that crawls on the window screen in the early days of spring. Both of these are useful beetles, helping, as do the birds, in keeping potentially harmful insects in check. The public, however, still seems to think that anything alive, unless they actually know it is useful, is something to kill. A great deal of our work for conservation must be educational. Most of our high school biology courses have a brief period taken in discussion of "insect pests," and even the teachers seem to be in considerable doubt that there are any insects that are not pests.

I have stated that insects are only potentially harmful under natural conditions. It is when the natural conditions are disturbed in some manner that insects become destructive. The first of these ways of destroying natural conditions is the introduction of an insect into a region where it does not naturally belong. The introduced insect's natural enemies are not brought along with it. The predatory and parasitic insects that are present do not have the instinct to attack the introduced insect, and this is also likely to be true of birds, toads, and other insect enemies. So the new insect's rate of reproduction is not checked by a correspondingly keen struggle for existence, and it increases tremendously.

Most of our worst insect pests are introduced species, though there are some cases where native insects become pests, and these occur where the natural conditions no longer apply. A good many insects are limited in the potential harm they can do by the fact that they live only on certain plants and no others. Although it would seem as if any plant could furnish them food, their instinct is such that they will actually starve if they cannot get the right plant. Usually they attack plants of one family only, and often of only one genus, and at times a single species. In most cases, the plant they feed upon grows scattered about the country, mixed with other kinds of plants. An adult insect, hunting its natural food plant for an opportunity to deposit its eggs, must fly some distance, and every moment of that flight is fraught with danger of destruction by one of its enemies. The scattered distribution of its food plant is one factor that makes its struggle for existence more keen.

If the food happens to be one that is useful to man, man plants it on a large scale, over a large area. The amount of the insect's food has been increased, and the distribution of it has been concentrated. When the insect finds the area planted by man, it can spread easily from plant to plant, and the danger from natural enemies is much less. So the insect increases in numbers and becomes destructive. This is one of the important reasons why insects, whether introduced species or native, have become pests. The boll weevil, corn borer, Hessian fly, potato beetle, and many others have spread tremendously for this reason. Some years ago certain railroad companies planted groves of locust trees along their rights of way, planning to utilize the land for the production of an excellent tie wood. Long before the trees reached a size to be of value, the locust borer, a common, native American insect, whose larva bores in locust wood only, killed practically all of these trees. No such destruction ever took place in native locust trees that grew in a natural forest scattered among many other kinds of trees.

Modern methods of agriculture and insect control teach that the edges and borders of planted fields should be kept clear of bushes, vines, weeds, or other growth. It is believed that these things take some of the richness from the soil and make places where insects are harbored or their eggs and larvae are concealed. While this may be more or less true, I believe there is another side to the question. A number of years ago I spent a summer vacation working on a farm. On this farm were two fields of potatoes. The first was near the center of the farm, and its edges were properly cleared of weeds, bushes, etc. Everything had been done, except spraying, to keep down potato beetles. The farmer had been too shorthanded for that, so we picked the potato beetles off by hand. They were numerous and had already done considerable damage.

The other field was back in a neglected corner. It was surrounded by stone walls, and these were overgrown with thick bushes and vines. In these bushes I noted song and field sparrows, towhees, indigo buntings, rose-breasted grosbeaks, yellow warblers, yellowthroats, catbirds, and thrashers. The potatoes were not growing well, for they were badly choked by weeds, but we found almost no potato beetles on them. The birds were evidently nesting in the bushes about the field and gleaning their food from the surrounding country. All of them are reported to be important destroyers of harmful insects. Several are especially noted as eaters of leaf beetles, and three, the catbird, towhee, and rose-breasted grosbeak, are credited with destruction of the potato beetle. The rose-breasted grosbeak is known in some regions as the "potato-bug bird," and a single pair has been known to keep a potato patch free of the beetles all summer. In my own opinion, thick bushes and vines along stone walls or fence rows are worth more as cover and nesting sites for insect-destroying birds than the richness they may take from the soil or the harm they may do in harboring insects.

Where civilization has destroyed natural conditions and birds or other insect enemies are scarce, or where introduced insects are spreading, I presume that spraying trees, bushes, and plants with various poisonous mixtures becomes necessary. But we often carry spraying too far, and naturally companies in the business of spraying or selling the apparatus and poisons encourage this. I do not know to what extent spraying injures birds directly or kills them. Reports are contradictory in this matter. One investigator claims that the amount of poison a bird would get by eating a poisoned insect is too small to do it any harm. Another report that came to me, rather thirdhand, was that after the spraying of city trees a number of dead starlings were found on roofs, and when someone protested to the spraying company the reply was that such things must be expected. One friend, who is a taxidermist, states that each year, shortly after city trees are sprayed, numbers of dead Baltimore orioles are brought to him with peculiar conditions of the internal organs that, he believes, are due to poison. I know of one street where the elm trees are sprayed annually but were not so sprayed when I first knew it. Since the spraying became a regular thing, the warbling vireos that used to live there have disappeared.

It is not proven that the direct killing of birds can come from ordinary poison sprays. But the destruction of all leaf-eating insects by the use of poison sprays can destroy so much of the food that birds depend on that birds must decrease in numbers where spraying is done. I am also inclined to think that the lack of birds in sprayed areas increases the numbers of sap-sucking insects that cannot be affected by such sprays.

The spraying of areas wholesale with such preparations as DDT is deplorable, for it destroys nearly all kinds of insects, both useful and harmful, and is definitely known to kill birds. I believe that if we are to save our bird life for the future the use of DDT should be regulated by law and strictly forbidden in natural forest areas, where the balance between insects and enemies is natural and can be maintained.

The spraying of natural forests is bad, whether DDT or some ordinary poison is used. I am reminded of a forested area I have known since boyhood. It never suffered from great damage by insects, for it was natural and left alone. But a few years ago, men, realizing the scenic beauty of the place, constructed an auto parkway through it, and a year or so later, as I drove along the parkway, I came upon a spraying crew, their apparatus mounted on an auto, busily spraying the trees as far back from the road as the apparatus could reach.

Partial spraying of a forest area is likely to be worse than no spraying at all. In an area where insects are destroyed and the birds gone because of spraying, the insects will recover sooner and come back quickly, because their life cycles are shorter and their rate of reproduction tremendously greater. The spraying is likely to be followed by insects coming into the sprayed area much sooner than birds, and increasing more rapidly because the birds are not there. For this same reason, the spraying of forest tops by airplane is likely to cause more insects in the long run, for the spraying cannot get to the whole tree, but only to its top. It will drive out the birds that live in the treetops and give the insects that escape a chance to recover rapidly.

There have been some arguments advanced that birds are of no importance as controllers of insects, that insect control is chiefly due to other insects, predatory or parasitic. I do not doubt the value of such insects in controlling harmful ones. But I have seen many cases where they were definitely controlled by birds; in fact, where very large numbers of insects were wiped out in a short time. This has happened with the tent caterpillar, in spite of its hairy covering. It happens often with spanworms when they occur for a time in unusual numbers. I have seen a row of shade trees, with almost every twig laden with eggs of the fall cankerworm in November, and been unable to find a single cluster or any of the caterpillars the following spring, owing to the winter activities of a flock of chickadees. Experiences like these lead me to believe that those who are combating harmful insects, on the theory that birds are not important in controlling them, have much more to learn.

The various things that threaten birds—and, for that matter, all forms of wildlife—with decrease in numbers or extinction may be put into two classes. These are the various ways of destroying or modifying the habitat in which birds live and nest, and the direct destruction of the birds themselves. The abundance of a species of bird, provided things are not done that destroy it directly, is determined by the area of its natural habitat; or, when that is changed, its adaptability to live in a modified habitat. A good many species do not have that adaptability. With some species it is not so much a matter of habitat as of available nesting sites. This would apply to swallows, and probably also to those sea birds that nest on rock ledges.

Man destroys or modifies bird habitats by cutting forests, by fire, by draining marshes and polluting streams, by poison sprays, by removing underbrush, cover, old logs, dead trees, dead limbs, and stumps. He also modifies habitats or the ecological conditions in them by destroying predators or introducing foreign species, or attempting to increase a species beyond the capacity of the habitat to support it. When man establishes a songbird sanctuary and protects it by shooting bird-killing hawks, owls, shrikes, etc., he has practically created a baited trap for these birds. This is particularly true in winter when he causes, by winter feeding, a concentration of birds in the spot, often without cover where they can take refuge from enemies. Winter-feeding stations should be accompanied by dense bushes, evergreens, or at least a brush pile as protection. In summer, even in a sanctuary, birds will not increase beyond the capacity of the area to support them naturally.

The question of the predatory hawk is one that should be considered from the standpoint of common sense rather than sentiment. The sharp-shinned and Cooper's hawks are birds too. Nature equipped them to kill for food, and they must do so or starve. They are no more cruel in their killing than a robin eating earthworms or a vireo eating caterpillars. If they were not killed by man, they would not increase to such an extent as to cause any species of wild bird to be in danger of extinction. They protect birds from becoming too numerous for their own good and weed out the weaker, unfit individuals, thereby insuring the best heredity for future generations. Our best-informed experts on game birds agree to these facts, and to the lack of any necessity to kill predators.

I realize that there are many who consider that the killing of predators is a part of conservation. Those who are propagating game so that sportsmen may have more to kill, and killing predators by shooting or pole traps, though they are often dignified under such a name as conservation commission, are not practicing conservation at all. Any kind of practice that requires the killing of one kind of wild creature in order to save another is not conservation and is based on a misunderstanding of the whole matter.

Just as in the case of the songbird sanctuary, game-breeding stations protected by guns or pole traps, or fish hatcheries where herons and kingfishers are attracted and then shot, are baited traps for our wildlife. Methods of protecting fish hatcheries from kingfishers and herons by wires through which they cannot get at the young fish have been developed and can be used. One prominent man in fish-hatchery work told me they could not afford this protecting apparatus. That was merely because the fishermen, and others who appropriate money for the work, value fish more highly than birds. But the aesthetic and recreational value of a great blue heron to the increasing number of bird lovers is greater than that of many fish. Each fish can be caught by one fisherman only and gives recreation to him alone, but each heron may be seen by dozens of bird lovers if allowed to live its life out. It is time we stopped the one-sidedness of our conservation efforts and considered all forms of wildlife at the same time. In most of our state game and conservation commissions, the bird lover is not represented. He does not pay a fee for a hunting and fishing license. But attempting to increase one kind of wildlife by destroying another is not conservation.

Fishermen often think that any animal or bird that obtains food from the water must necessarily be getting fish, and to him fish means game fish, such as bass or trout. But life in the water consists of many other things: water insects of many kinds, leeches, crayfish, snails, salamanders, tadpoles, and many small fish that never grow large enough for use by man but are perfectly good food for a fish-eating bird. Herons were being shot at a certain fish hatchery, and the manager was finally induced to examine the birds that were shot to see what they had been eating. The next three great blue herons shot had nothing but crayfish in their stomachs. Except at hatcheries where proper protection by wiring has not been established, fish-eating birds rarely get fish of any value to man.

In many places, even in thickly settled regions, there are areas of wild land that seem to have been forgotten and left to nature. Such places generally contain more wildlife, and more kinds of wildlife, than areas where man makes a special effort to save and protect it. I am thinking of one such area where I often go. It is within walking distance of a large industrial city, but it cannot be reached by walking on roads, only by cutting across areas where there is neither road nor path, and the going is often difficult. Thick undergrowth of blackberries and greenbrier protects a large part of the area from the nearest road to it, and on the other side is a large area of swamp and marsh. In that area there nest several kinds of hawks, and there are fox dens. In spite of this, there are ruffed grouse and rabbits in some numbers. The white birches have never had their bark cut off by vandals, and the beeches have beautiful smooth gray bark, unscarred by someone's initials. Ground pine carpets the forest floor as thickly as grass in a lawn, for no one tears it up to make Christmas wreaths. This place has never been "improved" or made into a sanctuary or advertised to the public. Consequently it is more truly a sanctuary than other places that have that name.

Old logs in the forest are drumming places for the ruffed grouse. They harbor snails, centipedes, ground beetles, salamanders, and they are places where fungi and mosses and ferns may grow. They gradually rot back into the soil and replace the elements that were taken out when the original tree grew. Yet it is supposed to be good forestry to remove them. So far as I know, the chief reason for their removal is that they would be in the way in case of logging operations.

Dead trees, limbs, and stumps in the forest are homes for woodpeckers, and woodpeckers are the chief controllers of borers, bark beetles, and other insects that are the only ones that can kill a big tree directly. In a few cases where bark beetles have killed a large area of forest, as happened in the Black Hills some years ago, I believe the explanation was that the dead trees were first removed. Insects that live in dead trees and fungi that grow on them do not attack live trees. Dead trees may be a fire menace, but in a dry season everything in the forest—leaves, litter, humus, moss—becomes a fire menace. Our best efforts at fire control would not be to change the natural conditions of the forest, but to control the chief fire menace, a biped that generally smokes cigarettes and has no notion of how and when a campfire is safe and when not.

There seems to be a prejudice in the minds of many people against bushes, shrubs, and small trees. To them a forest ought to be like a grove in a city park, with an open vista between the trees in all directions. Anyone who knows nature knows how comparatively birdless such a grove is. Undergrowth forms nesting sites and cover. Many more birds' nests are in bushes or under bushes than are in trees. Landscaping of original natural woods seems to consist mainly of removing everything that is less than a foot in diameter. Trees are apparently only of value when they are old and their lives are nearly over. It is good that we do not hold this same attitude in regard to people. I have known of cases where this kind of landscaping was done, where someone built his house in a wooded area. Numbers of the small trees cut down were flowering dogwoods. Then, after the house was built, the owner bought more dogwoods only differing from the original ones in that they were smaller and set out in straight, evenly spaced rows.

Drainage of marshes and swamps is sometimes necessary in the advance of civilization, but a very large part of that which has been done was not necessary and has not created land of greater value than the original swamp or marsh. We should think twice before we allow indiscriminate drainage of marshes and swamps. They are wonderful places for wildlife, and much of that wildlife can live nowhere else and will be extinct if we drain all such places. A good many places that were once the breeding grounds of wild ducks, bitterns, rails, and many desirable wild creatures are now only dreary wastes. The soil beneath them that was supposed to make valuable farms proved to be practically worthless.

When predatory species, thought by those who know little of nature to be undesirable, are destroyed, the reproduction rate of the animals they preyed upon goes on, those animals increase, and the result, sooner or later, is starvation. The well-known case of the Kaibab deer illustrates one phase of this, and the same sort of condition has occurred in a number of other cases. The troubles that come are not only starved deer, but destruction of many plants and young trees by the deer.

Meadow mice have a high rate of reproduction. In normal numbers they are harmless, but when too abundant they often girdle young trees by eating the bark in winter. Now meadow mice are preyed upon by hawks, owls, weasels, mink, skunks, foxes, and snakes. That is quite a list of wild creatures that the average man thinks should be destroyed or controlled. It is when men destroy too many of these creatures that meadow mice become numerous and do damage.

In past times ranchmen in the West grew wealthy in the business of raising sheep or cattle. They took care of the coyotes and wolves without undue losses to their stock. But now our less self-reliant people have to have help. They worked politics to have government bureaus, originally established to make scientific studies, become wildlife destroyers. The poisoning of coyotes that followed led to the necessity of jackrabbit drives and poisoning of ground squirrels, and this was followed by swarms of grasshoppers. Certainly, before any great effort is made to destroy a wild creature, a careful study of its food habits and ecological relations should be made.

Where civilization has changed conditions, animal life does at times become too numerous and control measures are needed. But as in the case of insects, we should keep in mind that that is not true in wild natural areas, and the efforts at control should be confined to cultivated areas and perhaps a buffer strip bordering those areas.

There is a certain bird sanctuary that contains a small pond. Mallard ducks nest about the pond and bring up their broods of young on it. In the pond are a number of spotted turtles. Skunks were not encouraged in this sanctuary, but were trapped and destroyed at every opportunity because they occasionally eat bird's eggs. But skunks also eat turtle's eggs and are one of the few checks on the increase of turtles that nature has given us. One year the pond had altogether too many turtles, and they, being hungry, attacked the newly hatched mallards, destroying two whole broods. Skunks in the sanctuary, even though they ate a few birds' eggs, would have kept such a thing from happening.

When a natural habitat contains all the life that belongs there—the predators, herbivores, and others, all adjusted to each other by their rates of reproduction—and a new kind of creature that does not naturally belong there is introduced and succeeds, it does so at the expense of some other native species. Another species cannot be crowded into the balance without something else succumbing to give it room. The bad results of introducing species in places where they do not belong have been known for years, yet people go on introducing them without first seeking advice from those who know wildlife. The starling and English sparrow in America, the rabbit and red deer in Australia, the muskrat in Europe, to say nothing of the most destructive of our insects, are well-known examples.

In my opinion, the chief harm in the introduction of the ring-necked pheasant is its bad effect upon the bob-white. The latter bird, in the North, has had to hold its own against a combination of hunters and hard winters and now must compete with the bigger, stronger pheasant for a place to live in its own natural habitat. Of course the pheasant is bigger and gaudier and easier to shoot, if that is what the sportman wants. But the bob-white is just as beautiful and less harmful to grains and fruits, quite useful as a controller of insects, and has a thousand times sweeter voice. We introduce a foreign game bird that crowds out a native one. We then kill our native hawks and owls because they prey on the foreign game bird, or we think they do. We do all this for the gratification of those people whose chief sport is found in killing something.

Too much killing of birds takes place chiefly in game birds, predators, and birds that have valuable plumage. Killing birds for plumage, in this country at least, seems to be mostly a thing of the past. When we license a large and unlimited number of men to go out each year and kill a certain few species, such as woodcock, grouse, bob-white, and ducks, the matter of conserving these species in normal numbers becomes increasingly difficult. The sportsmen seem to think that they can be safely entrusted with the conservation of game. Most of them seem to know next to nothing about wildlife, and nothing at all about ecology. They consider that they can protect and conserve game, however, and in the past boasted that if they are given an open season to hunt a particular kind of wildlife they will see that it is protected, but if not, they will do nothing to protect it. The increase and abundance of the bob-white in

Ohio since that state removed it from the game-bird list seems to be good evidence that we do not need the protection of the sportsmen. The recent increase of the shore birds that have been off the game-bird list for a number of years is another bit of evidence that what these birds needed mainly was protection from sportsmen.

There seems to be an idea on the part of some people that once a wild creature is reduced in numbers it will never again be numerous. This is true if the reduction is caused or accompanied by destruction of large areas of its natural habitat, but if the species has room and place in which to breed, it returns to normal numbers when the cause of its decrease is removed. This is attested by the recent increases of terns, and gulls, and egrets. But there is a low ebb to which species may go, from which they do not seem to recover, but go on to extinction in spite of efforts to save them. That has been the case with the passenger pigeon and the heath hen. We hope it will not be so with the whooping crane, trumpeter swan, roseate spoonbill, and a number of others that are at present in greatly reduced numbers. Each species goes through a cycle of years of abundance, followed by years of scarcity. While I doubt if that cycle is as regular and perfect as it is supposed to be, it exists, and there are lean years. When a species is greatly reduced and the lean years come, it is likely to go out altogether. We should give all species such protection that their numbers will always be great enough to survive the low ebb of the cycle.

One of the things we must consider in the conservation of game birds and of predators and other large birds is the attitude of the average sportsman. There are altogether too many who are granted hunting licenses each year but have no intention of abiding by the game laws except when forced to do so by the presence of a game warden. Such men are not always ignorant or impecunious. Sometimes they are wealthy men, prominent in business or politics, who seem to think that their money or position ought to give them the right to kill what they please, where or whenever they want to. In recent discussions concerning the decrease of ducks, it was reported that certain men had no interest in saving ducks for the future, but only in killing all they could before they were all gone. It is time that we stressed the rights of naturalists and bird lovers to wild ducks alive, and in sufficient numbers to enjoy the sight of them frequently.

I have spoken harshly of sportsmen, but I realize that there are some who deserve no such criticism, who abide by the laws and realize that these laws are for their own greatest good. Yet even some of these seem to condone the lawless attitude of other sportsmen and listen to their boasts of how they break the laws without protest. Another attitude is that the game belongs to the sportsmen and that nature lovers and naturalists should have nothing to say about it. Do not the game wardens, supported by the sportsmen, protect songbirds for the nature lovers? Theoretically they do, but actually, today, sentiment is the greatest protector of songbirds. So far as direct killing is concerned, songbirds are rarely in need of protection. These attitudes on the part of sportsmen are gradually producing among other people an antagonism against sportsmen and hunting and might result someday in making hunting illegal. That is why, if sportsmen wish to continue to hunt, they should pay more attention to clearing their ranks of those whose attitude is wrong. I believe that in some future day, if hunting is to continue, limiting the number of hunting licenses must come, and that the limitations will be brought about by refusing licenses to those whose attitudes toward game laws are wrong and to those whose ignorance of wildlife is so great that they shoot at any large bird that flies and find out later whether it can be legally killed or not.

I might suggest to the sportsman who fears that his outdoor recreation may be gone in the near future that he try hunting birds with a binocular. Then he will not be limited as to season, number, or kind of species he finds, and there will be no danger that finding something rare and thrilling will contribute to its scarcity or extinction. He will find live birds a thousand times more beautiful and interesting than dead bodies. He will bring back memories not stained with the sight of sudden death or painful crippling of living creatures, but brightened with the joy of living creatures, still alive to give pleasure to someone else.

There are numbers of kinds of animals whose food habits are such that, though useful much of the time, they are sometimes, when in contact with civilization, harmful to man's interests. Such creatures, such as the crow, for example, cannot be given legal protection, for farmers should have the right to protect their crops from depredations. But the fact that the crow is not so protected is no reason for attempting to destroy it wholesale, by crow shoots or dynamiting crow roosts. The crow is a quite able bird and will probably never be in danger of extermination, despite all the propaganda against it. The attitude that

Sharp-tailed sparrow

attempts to destroy it in numbers, that inflames people against it by exaggerated statements as to its harm, is wrong. Crows are not "black villains," they are merely wild living creatures striving to find their food and keep alive in the only ways they know. When finding something edible and consuming it works harm instead of benefit to man, they cannot be expected to know the difference. It is only man, who has reason as well as instinct to guide him, who can be expected to know the difference between right and wrong.

There is an attitude common to man, to blame some kind of predator when he finds some useful animal decreasing. We are told that ducks are scarce because crows eat their eggs; ruffed grouse are gone in certain areas because goshawks and foxes kill them all; salmon are decreasing because eagles and bears eat them. We forget that these creatures have always done these things and that their prey did not decrease through long ages until very recently. Each bear eats only enough salmon to relieve his hunger. It is only man who kills much more than he can eat immediately. We cannot save a natural resource by putting the blame for its decrease in the wrong place. The salmon interests could, if allowed to do so, exterminate the bears and the eagles, and then continue and exterminate the salmon.

On a certain reef there are great numbers of edible mussels, and every winter quantities of gulls feed on them. Men seldom gather them for food. But during the depression days, when men were out of work and had little money to buy food, many began gathering the mussels. Not long after that the mussels became scarce. Then men began to ask why gulls should be protected by law, when *they* were eating up all the mussels.

We have set aside national parks, state parks, sanctuaries, bird reservations, game preserves, and many areas where wildlife is more or less protected. Most of these areas are forest or mountainous country, or swamps and marshes. Some of our most desirable forms of wild life, however, live in open country, grassy prairies and plains, salt marsh, sagebrush, and similar areas that, drained or cultivated, can be converted to places desirable for civilization. We could spare a few such areas for the sake of the wild creatures that prefer them and in many cases could not live elsewhere. The sage hen, the long-billed curlew, the upland plover, and smaller species such as the longspurs are ones that live in prairie regions and could be saved there. In the past twenty years I have watched civilization gradually reducing the areas of salt marsh in a highly civilized region. They are drained or filled in to develop real estate for shore cottages or parking grounds near a populous sea beach. In the course of such reduction, clapper rails and seaside and sharp-tailed sparrows have smaller and smaller areas in which to live. The salt-marsh sparrows are not brilliantly colored, nor great singers, and they are totally unknown to the public and even to many bird lovers. If they go into extinction, almost no one will care. Definitely setting aside a few areas of salt marsh, in such manner that no commercial or political scheme can touch or despoil them in the future, would save these birds.

I would suggest that for the future good of our country we need a definitely planned conservation scheme that will set aside areas of every natural habitat in every state and make them all inviolate, not merely for the saving of wildlife on them, but for saving every detail of wild conditions. We should make this so strong that it would be out of the power of Congress or any other body or official to consider encroachment on the area for either commercial or any other use than that for which it is set aside. Such areas would protect not only birds, but many forms of animals and wild plants.

These areas should be protected from drainage, fire, removal of old logs, dead trees, or limbs, practice of tree surgery or forestry, application of poison sprays, cutting, thinning, or trimming of shrubbery, introduction of foreign species, or building roads or trails across the area. The areas should not be advertised to the general public as places to visit or picnic. Paths may lead into and out of the area, but not across it, so that no one should go through it to get somewhere else.

So the matter of saving live birds for the future, birds that can give to man great pleasure, a saner life, an uplifting of ideals, a deeper insight into the wonders of this world and the life it holds, and a revelation of the higher power that caused it all, is to be solved by saving, in their natural conditions, areas of wild land. Thus we can protect from slaughter all those species that man picks out as ones to kill. Thus we can educate the coming generations in the love of wild creatures that are alive, so that as the years advance we may do less killing and more observing of the living bird.

Bibliography

INTRODUCTION

Some books that treat of the lives of birds

Allen, Arthur A., *The Book of Bird Life,* D. Van Nostrand Co., New York, 1930.

Griscom, Ludlow, *Modern Bird Study,* Harvard University Press, Cambridge, 1945.

Hickey, Joseph J., *A Guide to Bird Watching,* Oxford University Press, New York, 1943.

Pettingill, Olin Sewell, *A Laboratory and Field Manual of Ornithology,* Burgess Publishing Co., Minneapolis, 1946.

SOME GENERAL BOOKS ON BIRDS

Bailey, Florence Merriam, *Birds of Mexico,* New Mexico Department of Game and Fish, Santa Fe, 1928. A good source of information on birds of the Southwest.

Bent, Arthur Cleveland, *Life Histories of North American Birds,* Bulletins of the United States National Museum, Washington, D.C., 1919–53.

At the present time this work consists of twenty volumes, covering all species of North American birds from the loons through the warblers. A large part of the remainder is in manuscript. This is a co-operative work to which many have contributed.

Forbush, Edward Howe, *The Birds of Massachusetts and Other New England States,* 3 vols., published by the Commonwealth of Massachusetts, 1925, 1927, 1929.

A valuable reference work, containing much information and excellent colored plates by Louis Agassiz Fuertes and Alan Brooks.

Roberts, Thomas S., *The Birds of Minnesota,* University of Minnesota Press, 1932. Contains much information and excellent colored plates.

Stone, Witmer, *The Birds of Old Cape May,* 2 vols., published by the Delaware Valley Ornithological Club at the Academy of Natural Sciences, Philadelphia, 1937.

IDENTIFICATION

Hausman, Leon Augustus, *Field Book of Eastern Birds,* G. P. Putnam's Sons, New York, 1946.

Hoffmann, Ralph, *Birds of the Pacific States,* Houghton Mifflin Co., Boston, 1927.

Peterson, Roger Tory, *A Field Guide to the Birds,* Houghton Mifflin Co., Boston, 1934. Revised editions were printed in 1939 and 1947.

———, *A Field Guide to Western Birds,* Houghton Mifflin Co., Boston, 1941.

Pough, Richard H., *Audubon Bird Guide,* Doubleday & Co., New York, 1946.

———, *Audubon Water Bird Guide,* Doubleday & Co., New York, 1951.

MIGRATION

Ball, Stanley C., *Fall Bird Migration on the Gaspé Peninsula,* Peabody Museum of Natural History, Yale University, Bulletin 7, New Haven, 1952.

Chapman, Frank M., *Travels of Birds,* D. Appleton & Co., New York, 1916.

Cooke, Wells W., *Bird Migration,* U. S. Department of Agriculture, Bulletin 185, Washington, D.C., 1915.

Lewis, Harrison F., "Reverse Migration," *Auk,* Vol. 56, pp. 13–27, 1939.

Lincoln, Frederick C., *Migration of Birds,* Doubleday & Co., New York, 1952.

Rowan, William, *Riddle of Migration,* Williams & Wilkins Co., Baltimore, 1931.

Tyler, Winsor M., "The Call-notes of Some Nocturnal Migrating Birds," *Auk,* Vol. 33, pp. 132–41, 1916.

Wetmore, Alexander, *Migration of Birds,* Harvard University Press, Cambridge, 1926.

THE NESTING CYCLE

Bergtold, W. H., *A Study of the Incubation Periods of Birds,* Kendrick Bellamy Co., Denver, 1917.

Bibliography

Howard, H. Eliot, *Territory in Bird Life,* John Murray, London; E. P. Dutton & Co., New York, 1920.

Mousley, Henry, "The Singing Tree or How Near to the Nests Do the Male Birds Sing?" *Auk,* Vol. 36, pp. 339–438, 1919.

———, "Which Sex Selects the Nesting Locality?" *Auk,* Vol. 38, pp. 321–28, 1921.

Nice, Margaret Morse, *Studies in the Life History of the Song Sparrow,* Translations of the Linnaean Society of New York, Vol. IV, 1937.

Saunders, Aretas A., *Studies of Breeding Birds in the Allegany State Park,* New York State Museum Bulletin No. 318, 1938.

Townsend, Charles W., "Courtship in Birds," *Auk,* Vol. 37, pp. 380–93, 1920.

STUDYING BIRDS' NESTS

Glover, Fred A., *Nesting Ecology of the Pied-billed Grebe in Northwestern Iowa,* Wilson Bulletin 65, pp. 32–39, 1953.

Hann, Harry W., *Life History of the Ovenbird in Southern Michigan,* Wilson Bulletin 49, pp. 145–237, 1937.

Herrick, Francis Hobart, *Wild Birds at Home,* D. Appleton-Century Co., New York, 1935.

Howell, Thomas R., "Natural History and Differentiation in the Yellow-bellied Sapsucker," *Condor,* Vol. 54, pp. 237–82, 1952.

Mousley, Henry, "Home Life of the American Goldfinch," *Canadian Field Naturalist,* pp. 177–79, 338–45, 1930.

Nice, Margaret M., *A Study of the Nesting of Magnolia Warblers,* Wilson Bulletin 38, pp. 185–99, 1926.

Odum, Eugene, "Annual Cycle of the Black-capped Chickadee," *Auk,* Vol. 58, pp. 314–33; Vol. 59, pp. 501–5, 1941–42.

Saunders, Aretas A., "A Study of the Nesting of the Cedar Waxwing," *Auk,* Vol. 28, pp. 323–29, 1911.

Stanwood, Cordelia J., "The Black-throated Green Warbler," *Auk,* Vol. 27, pp. 289–94, 1910.

Walkinshaw, Lawrence H., "Studies of the Short-billed Marsh Wren in Michigan," *Auk,* Vol. 52, pp. 362–69, 1935.

BIRD BEHAVIOR

Grinnell, Joseph, "Sequestration Notes," *Auk,* Vol. 38, pp. 198–203, 1920.

———, "The Principle of Rapid Peering in Birds," *University of California Chronicle* 23, pp. 393–96, 1921.

The above two papers have been reprinted in Joseph Grinnell's *Philosophy of Nature,* University of California Press, Berkeley, 1943.

Hochbaum, Albert H., *The Canvasback on a Prairie Marsh,* American Wild Life Institute, Washington, D.C., 1944.

MacAtee, W. L., "Anting," *Auk,* Vol. 55, pp. 98–105, 1936.

Nice, Margaret M., *Studies in the Life History of the Song Sparrow,* Transactions of the Linnaean Society of New York, Vol. VI, 1943.

Nicholson, Edward M., *The Art of Bird-Watching,* H. F. and G. Witherby, London, 1931.

Palmer, William, "Instinctive Stillness in Birds," *Auk,* Vol. 26, pp. 23–36, 1909.

Bibliography

Poole, Earl L., "A Graphic Method of Recording Flight," *Auk*, Vol. 42, pp. 209–16, 1925.

Tinbergen, N., *The Study of Instinct,* Oxford University Press, New York, 1951.

Tyler, Winsor M., "Simultaneous Action in Birds. A Suggestion," *Auk,* Vol. 32, pp. 198–203, 1915.

PLUMAGES AND FEATHERS

Dwight, Jonathan, *Sequence of Plumages and Moults of the Passerine Birds of New York,* Annals of the New York Academy of Sciences, Vol. 3, pp. 73–360, 1900.

Thayer, Abbot H. and Gerald B., *Concealing Coloration in the Animal Kingdom,* Macmillan Co., New York, 1909.

SONGS AND CALLS

Albert R. Brand Bird Song Foundation, *American Bird Songs,* Vols. 1 and 2, Comstock Publishing Associates. Phonograph disks containing songs and calls of 72 species (Vol. 1) and 51 species (Vol. 2).

Brand, Albert R., *Songs of Wild Birds,* Thomas Nelson and Sons, New York, 1934. With phonograph records from wild birds.

———, *More Songs of Wild Birds,* Thomas Nelson and Sons, New York, 1936. With phonograph records from wild birds.

Craig, Wallace, *The Song of the Wood Pewee. A Study of Bird Music,* New York State Museum Bulletin No. 334, Albany, 1943.

Mathews, F. Schuyler, *Field Book of Wild Birds and Their Music,* G. P. Putnam's Sons, New York, 1904.

Saunders, Aretas A., *Bird Song,* New York State Museum Handbook No. 7, Albany, 1929.

————, *Guide to Bird Songs,* Doubleday & Co., New York, 1951.

————, "The Seasons of Bird Song," *Auk,* Vol. 64, pp. 97–107, 1947–48, and Vol. 65, pp. 19–30 and 373–83.

Stillwell, Jerry and Norma, *Bird Songs of Dooryard, Field and Forest,* 1953. One long-playing phonograph disk with songs and calls of 49 species.

FOOD OF BIRDS

Baumgartner, Marguerite, *Food and Feeding Habits of the Tree Sparrow,* Wilson Bulletin 49, pp. 65–80, 1937.

Beal, F. E. L., *Birds as Conservators of Forests,* Report of the New York State Forest, Fish, and Game Commission, 1902–3, pp. 236–74, Albany, 1906.

Fisher, A. K., *The Hawks and Owls of the United States,* U. S. Department of Agriculture, Division of Ornithology and Mammalogy, Bulletin 3, Washington, D.C., 1893.

Forbes, S. A., *The Regulative Action of Birds upon Insect Oscillation,* Bulletin of the Illinois State Laboratory of Natural History, Vol. 1, No. 6, 1883.

Henderson, Junius, *The Practical Value of Birds,* Macmillan Co., New York, 1927.

MacAtee, W. L., *The Relation of Birds to Woodlots,* Roosevelt Wild Life Bulletin, Vol. 4, No. 1, 1926.

Bibliography

ECOLOGY

Adams, Charles C., "The Ecological Succession of Birds," *Auk*, Vol. 25, 109–53, 1908.

Allen, Arthur A., *The Red-Winged Blackbird. A Study in the Ecology of a Cattail Marsh*, Proceedings of the Linnaean Society of New York, 1911–13, pp. 43–128, 1914.

Elton, Charles, *Animal Ecology*, Macmillan Co., New York, 1927.

Saunders, Aretas A., *Ecology of the Birds of Quaker Run Valley*, Allegany State Park, N.Y., New York State Museum Handbook 16, 1936.

Shelford, V. E., *Animal Communities in Temperate America*, Geographical Society of Chicago, Bulletin No. 5, 1913.

Williams, Arthur B., *Composition and Dynamics of a Beech-maple Climax Community*, Ecological Monographs, Vol. 6, No. 3, 1936.

CONSERVATION

Gabrielson, Ira N., *Wildlife Conservation*, Macmillan Co., New York, 1940.

———, *Wildlife Refuges*, Macmillan Co., New York, 1943.

Graham, Edward H., *Land and Wildlife*, Oxford University Press, New York, 1947.

Grinnell, Joseph, "A Conservationist's Creed as to Wild Life Administration," *Science*, Vol. 62, pp. 434–38, 1925.

———, "Tree Surgery and the Birds," *University of California Chronicle* 28, 104–6, 1927.

The above two papers are reprinted in Joseph Grinnell's *Philosophy of Nature,* University of California Press, Berkeley, 1943.

Hornaday, William T., *Our Vanishing Wild Life,* Charles Scribner's Sons, New York, 1913.

———, *Wild Life Conservation in Theory and Practice,* Yale University Press, New Haven, 1915.

Vogt, William, *Thirst on the Land,* Circular of the National Audubon Society, No. 32, 1937.

List of Species

REFERRED TO IN THIS BOOK

Common Loon. *Gavia immer.*
Pied-billed Grebe. *Podilymbus podiceps.*
Great Blue Heron. *Ardea herodias.*
American Egret. *Casmerodias albus.*
Black-crowned Night Heron. *Nycticorax nycticorax.*
American Bittern. *Botaurus lentiginosus.*
Least Bittern. *Ixobrychus exilis.*
Roseate Spoonbill. *Ajaja ajaja.*
Trumpeter Swan. *Cygnus buccinator.*
Mallard. *Anas platyrhynchos.*
Black Duck. *Anas rubripes.*
Blue-winged Teal. *Anas discors.*
Wood Duck. *Aix sponsa.*
Goshawk. *Astur atricapillus.*
Sharp-shinned Hawk. *Accipiter striatus.*
Cooper's Hawk. *Accipiter cooperi.*
Red-shouldered Hawk. *Buteo lineatus.*
Swainson's Hawk. *Buteo swainsoni.*
Marsh Hawk. *Circus hudsonius.*
Osprey. *Pandion haliaetus.*

Duck Hawk. *Falco peregrinus.*
Pigeon Hawk. *Falco columbarius.*
Sparrow Hawk. *Falco sparverius.*
Spruce Partridge. *Canachites canadensis.*
Franklin's Grouse. *Canachites franklini.*
Ruffed Grouse. *Bonasa umbellus.*
White-tailed Ptarmigan. *Lagopus leucurus.*
Heath Hen. *Tympanuchus cupido.*
Sage Hen. *Centrocercus urophasianus.*
Bob-white. *Colinus virginianus.*
Ring-necked Pheasant. *Phasianus colchicus.*
Whooping Crane. *Grus americana.*
Clapper Rail. *Rallus longirostris.*
Florida Gallinule. *Gallinula chloropus.*
Killdeer. *Charadrius vociferus.*
Ruddy Turnstone. *Arenaria interpres.*
Woodcock. *Philohela minor.*
Wilson's Snipe. *Capella gallinago.*
Long-billed Curlew. *Numenius americanus.*
Upland Plover. *Bartramia longicauda.*
Spotted Sandpiper. *Actitis macularia.*
Willet. *Catoptrophorus semipalmatus.*
Greater Yellowlegs. *Totanus melanoleucus.*
Lesser Yellowlegs. *Totanus flavipes.*
Least Sandpiper. *Erolia minutilla.*
Semipalmated Sandpiper. *Ereunetes pusillus.*
Sanderling. *Crocethia alba.*
Herring Gull. *Larus argentatus.*
Ring-billed Gull. *Larus delawarensis.*
Laughing Gull. *Larus atricilla.*
Black Tern. *Chlidonias niger.*
Passenger Pigeon. *Ectopistes migratorius.*
Yellow-billed Cuckoo. *Coccyzus americanus.*

Barn Owl. *Tyto alba.*
Screech Owl. *Otus asio.*
Snowy Owl. *Nyctea scandiaca.*
Short-eared Owl. *Asio flammeus.*
Whip-poor-will. *Antrostomus vociferus.*
Ruby-throated Hummingbird. *Archilocus colubris.*
Belted Kingfisher. *Megaceryle alcyon.*
Flicker. *Colaptes auratus.*
Hairy Woodpecker. *Dendrocopus villosus.*
Downy Woodpecker. *Dendrocopus pubescens.*
Kingbird. *Tyrannus tyrannus.*
Phoebe. *Sayornis phoebe.*
Alder Flycatcher. *Empidonax trailli.*
Least Flycatcher. *Empidonax minimus.*
Wood Pewee. *Contopus virens.*
Olive-sided Flycatcher. *Nuttallornis mesoleucus.*
Northern Horned Lark. *Otocoris alpestris alpestris.*
Prairie Horned Lark. *Otocoris alpestris praticola.*
Tree Swallow. *Iridoprocne bicolor.*
Barn Swallow. *Hirundo rustica.*
Blue Jay. *Cyanocitta cristata.*
Magpie. *Pica pica.*
Crow. *Corvus brachyrhynchos.*
Fish Crow. *Corvus ossifragus.*
Black-capped Chickadee. *Parus atricapillus.*
Brown Creeper. *Certhia familiaris.*
Dipper. *Cinclus mexicanus.*
House Wren. *Troglodytes aedon.*
Carolina Wren. *Thryothorus ludovicianus.*
Long-billed Marsh Wren. *Telmatodytes palustris.*
Mockingbird. *Mimus polyglottus.*
Catbird. *Dumetella carolinensis.*
Brown Thrasher. *Toxostoma rufum.*

List of Species

American Robin. *Turdus migratorius.*
Wood Thrush. *Hylocichla mustelina.*
Hermit Thrush. *Hylocichla guttata.*
Veery. *Hylocichla fuscescens.*
Bluebird. *Sialia sialis.*
Townsend's Solitaire. *Myadestes townsendi.*
Blue-gray Gnatcatcher. *Polioptila caerulea.*
Golden-crowned Kinglet. *Regulus satrapa.*
Ruby-crowned Kinglet. *Regulus calendula.*
American Pipit. *Anthus spinoletta.*
Tree Pipit. *Anthus trivialis.*
Sprague's Pipit. *Anthus spraguei.*
Cedar Waxwing. *Bombycilla cedrorum.*
Northern Shrike. *Lanius excubitor.*
Starling. *Sturnus vulgaris.*
White-eyed Vireo. *Vireo griseus.*
Blue-headed Vireo. *Vireo solitarius.*
Red-eyed Vireo. *Vireo olivaceus.*
Warbling Vireo. *Vireo gilvus.*
Black and White Warbler. *Mniotilta varia.*
Worm-eating Warbler. *Helmitherus vermivorus.*
Blue-winged Warbler. *Vermivora pinus.*
Yellow Warbler. *Dendroica petechia.*
Magnolia Warbler. *Dendroica magnolia.*
Black-throated Blue Warbler. *Dendroica caerulescens.*
Myrtle Warbler. *Dendroica coronata.*
Audubon's Warbler. *Dendroica auduboni.*
Black-throated Green Warbler. *Dendroica virens.*
Blackburnian Warbler. *Dendroica fusca.*
Chestnut-sided Warbler. *Dendroica pensylvanica.*
Blackpoll Warbler. *Dendroica striata.*
Palm Warbler. *Dendroica palmarum.*
Ovenbird. *Seiurus aurocapillus.*

Louisiana Water Thrush. *Seiurus motacilla.*
Mourning Warbler. *Oporornis philadelphia.*
Yellowthroat. *Geothlypis trichas.*
Yellow-breasted Chat. *Icteria virens.*
Hooded Warbler. *Wilsonia citrina.*
Pileolated Warbler. *Wilsonia pusilla pileolata.*
Canada Warbler. *Wilsonia canadensis.*
Redstart. *Setophaga ruticilla.*
English Sparrow. *Passer domesticus.*
Bobolink. *Dolichonyx oryzivorus.*
Eastern Meadowlark. *Sturnella magna.*
Yellow-headed Blackbird. *Xanthocephalus xanthocephalus.*
Redwing. *Agelaius phoeniceus.*
Baltimore Oriole. *Icterus galbula.*
Cowbird. *Molothrus ater.*
Scarlet Tanager. *Piranga olivacea.*
Summer Tanager. *Piranga rubra.*
Cardinal. *Richmondina cardinalis.*
Rose-breasted Grosbeak. *Pheucticus ludovicianus.*
Indigo Bunting. *Passerina cyanea.*
Purple Finch. *Carpodacus purpureus.*
Pine Grosbeak. *Pinicola enucleator.*
Gray-crowned Rosy Finch. *Leucosticte tephrocotis tephrocotis.*
Hepburn's Rosy Finch. *Leucosticte tephrocotis littoralis.*
Redpoll. *Acanthis flammea.*
Pine Siskin. *Spinus pinus.*
Goldfinch. *Spinus tristis.*
Towhee. *Pipilo erythrophthalmus.*
Lark Bunting. *Calamospiza melanocorys.*
Sharp-tailed Sparrow. *Ammospiza caudacuta.*
Seaside Sparrow. *Ammospiza maritima.*
Vesper Sparrow. *Pooecetes gramineus.*
Slate-colored Junco. *Junco hyemalis.*

List of Species

Tree Sparrow. *Spizella arborea.*
Field Sparrow. *Spizella pusilla.*
White-crowned Sparrow. *Zonotrichia leucophrys.*
Fox Sparrow. *Passerella iliaca.*
Lincoln's Sparrow. *Melospiza lincolni.*
Song Sparrow. *Melospiza melodia.*
McCown's Longspur. *Rhynchophanes mccowni.*
Snow Bunting. *Plectrophenax nivalis.*

Index

Index